Discover
China

WORKBOOK ONE

练习册 1

Contents

Lesson 3	Character writing
	• Practise 14 characters following seven rules of stroke order 十、丰、人、八、川、江、三、丁、月、问、回、国、小、水 • Learn to write Chinese numbers 四、五、六、七、九
• **Conversation:** greet people for the first time • **Character reading:** recognize characters with radicals 亻 and 女 • **Character writing:** introduce people • **Vocabulary extension:** use different terms of address for people	• Practise six characters with radicals 亻 and 女 你们、他、她、好、姓 • Learn to write seven common words for greetings and introductions 中文、什么、名字、认识、高兴、对不起、请问
• **Conversation:** exchange personal information about where you live • **Character reading:** recognize characters with radicals 口 and 日 • **Character writing:** ask questions about where people come from • **Vocabulary extension:** countries and places	• Practise five characters with radicals 口 and 日 叫、吗、明星、是 • Learn to write nine common words for greetings, nationalities and where people live 早上、不、但、哪里、住、在、北京、美国、英国
• **Conversation:** ask questions about people's families • **Character reading:** recognize characters with radicals 宀 and 阝 (right) • **Character writing:** write about occupations • **Vocabulary extension:** occupations	• Practise five characters with radicals 宀 and 阝 (right) 家、安、字、都、那 • Learn to write ten common words for family members and jobs 爸、妈、姐、妹、哥、弟、工作、医生、老师、学生
• **Conversation:** talk about favourite people • **Character reading:** recognize characters with radicals 土 and 氵 • **Character writing:** describe where people live • **Vocabulary extension:** expressions used to describe people	• Practise six characters with radicals 土 and 氵 出生地、上海、漂亮、在、法国、演员 • Learn to write seven common words for describing people's appearance 高、可爱、帅、酷、年轻、矮（漂亮）
• **Writing:** ask for addresses and contact numbers • **Character reading:** recognize characters with radicals 讠 and 辶 • **Character writing:** write about contact numbers • **Vocabulary extension:** words for addresses	• Practise six characters with radicals 讠 and 辶 记者、谁、这、发送、退出（话） • Learn to write seven common words for addresses and contact numbers 电话、号码、多少、地址、路、公寓、房间
• **Vocabulary:** public holidays in China • **Character reading:** recognize characters with radicals 月 and 扌 • **Character writing:** write about everyday activities • **Vocabulary extension:** days and dates	• Practise four characters with radicals 月 and 扌 月、星期、打、护士 • Learn to write nine common words for dates and daily activities 今天、几号、吃饭、去、学、做、见面、看书、上班

Lesson 3	Character writing
• **Reading:** understand people's weekly plans • **Character reading:** recognize characters with radicals 门 and 足 • **Character writing:** plan social activities • **Vocabulary extension:** leisure activities	• Practise four characters with radicals 门 and 足 跑步、时间、门、跟 • Learn to write ten common words for time expressions and daily activities 分、刻、半、点、中午、电影、晚、音乐、唱歌（跑步）
• **Listening:** understand an introduction from a shop assistant • **Character reading:** recognize characters with radicals 礻 and 贝 • **Character writing:** write about shopping • **Vocabulary extension:** items of clothing	• Practise eight characters with radicals 礻 and 贝 裙、裤、衬衫、售货员、贵、购 • Learn to write eight common words for clothes, colours and places 衣服、鞋、红、黑、蓝、白、超市、店
• **Reading:** understand descriptions of weekend activities • **Character reading:** recognize characters with radicals 木 and 彳 • **Character writing:** give directions • **Vocabulary extension:** places in the neighbourhood	• Practise five characters with radicals 木 and 彳 很、银行、往、楼、手机 • Learn to write nine common words for directions and types of student housing 东边、南、西、北、前、后、附近、房、宿舍
• **Conversation and listening:** understand dinner plans • **Character reading:** recognize characters with radicals 又 and 饣 • **Character writing:** make appointments • **Vocabulary extension:** places related to transport	• Practise seven characters with radicals 又 and 饣 喜欢、头发、对、朋友、双、饭馆 • Learn to write six common words for modes of transport and holiday activities 火车、旅行、爬山、参观、拍照、船
• **Conversation:** talk about a recreational class • **Character reading:** recognize characters with radicals 王 and 钅 • **Character writing:** describe recreational activities • **Vocabulary extension:** different types of sport	• Practise six characters with radicals 王 and 钅 玩、现在、班、足球、钱、地铁 • Learn to write seven common words for abilities and types of sports 可以、会、游泳、网球、踢、乒乓（足球）
• **Conversation and listening:** talk about travel experiences • **Character reading:** recognize characters with radicals 竹 and 禾 • **Character writing:** make plans for recreational activities • **Vocabulary extension:** holiday activities	• Practise five characters with radicals 竹 and 禾 打算、篮球、和、租、香港 • Learn to write six common words for places and holiday activities 地方、城市、西安、好玩、历史、主意

Getting started
Experiencing Chinese

LESSON | 1

Objectives

1 **Pinyin:** identify initials

2 **Pinyin:** identify finals

3 **Pronunciation and listening:** identify the four tones

4 **Pronunciation and listening:** identify the neutral tone

5 **Vocabulary and pronunciation:** Chinese numbers 1 to 10 and their tones

6 **Vocabulary and pronunciation:** Chinese numbers 1 to 10 and their pinyin

7 **Conversation:** common expressions

Pinyin

1 Circle the initials of the pinyin syllables.

1	tā	7	wén
2	de	8	zì
3	lǐ	9	zhōng
4	miàn	10	huá
5	cái	11	kàn
6	néng	12	shū

2 Circle the finals of the pinyin syllables.

1	lù	6	xī
2	sè	7	xiàn
3	hǎo	8	zuò
4	rén	9	fàn
5	dōng	10	guǎn

Pronunciation and listening

3 Listen and circle the characters with the same tones.

	ni	jiu	qi
1	你	九	七
	wu	si	er
2	五	四	二
	ren	mei	wo
3	人	没	我
	xie	san	wen
4	谢	三	问
	yi	yuan	sheng
5	医	院	生
	er	ying	xue
6	儿	英	学
	qing	bei	hao
7	请	贝	好
	ma	shi	dui
8	妈	师	对

Now listen again and add tones to the pinyin syllables.

4 Listen and circle the characters with the neutral tone.

shenme
1 什么

mama
4 妈妈

hao ma
2 好 吗

ni ne
5 你 呢

baba
3 爸爸

nanbian
6 南边

Now listen again and add tones to the pinyin syllables.

Vocabulary and pronunciation

5 Match the Chinese numbers with the English ones.

1 二		**a** one
2 五		**b** two
3 七		**c** three
4 八		**d** four
5 三		**e** five
6 九		**f** six
7 四		**g** seven
8 一		**h** eight
9 十		**i** nine
10 六		**j** ten

Now complete the table with the Chinese numbers.

Tones	Chinese numbers
1st tone	
2nd tone	
3rd tone	
4th tone	

6 Write down the numbers you hear in figures.

1 _____ _____

2 _____ _____

3 _____ _____

4 _____ _____

5 _____ _____

6 _____ _____

Now listen again and write pinyin for each number, including the correct tone.

Conversation

7 Complete the conversations with the expressions in the box.

bù kèqi	méiguānxi	zàijiàn
不 客气	没关系	再见

Zàijiàn
1 A: 再见！

B: _____ !

Xièxie
2 A: 谢谢！

B: _____ 。

Duì bu qǐ
3 A: 对不起。

B: _____ 。

LESSON | 2

Objectives

1 **Character reading:** recognize basic Chinese characters

2 **Character reading:** recognize radicals in Chinese characters

3 **Character writing:** the basic strokes

4 **Character writing:** the seven rules of stroke order

Character reading

1 Match the characters with the possible meanings.

1  口   **a** sky

2  上   **b** mouth

3  下   **c** big

4 中   **d** up

5 人   **e** middle

6  大   **f** down

7 天   **g** person

2 Identify the radicals of the characters.

1 林 lín   **a** crowd

2 森 sēn   **b** burn

3 众 zhòng   **c** woods

4 从 cóng   **d** flame

5 焚 fén   **e** forest

6 炎 yán   **f** follow

7 明 míng   **g** friend

8 朋 péng   **h** bright

Now match the characters with the possible meanings.

Character writing

3 Identify the basic strokes in the characters.

1 六   4 人

2 三   5 八

3 中   6 打

4 Match the characters with the correct stroke orders.

1 十   **a** from outside to inside, then closing

2 人   **b** from left to right

3 川   **c** horizontal before vertical

4 丁   **d** middle before two sides

5 问   **e** downward left before downward right

6 回   **f** from top to bottom

7 小   **g** from outside to inside

CHARACTER WRITING

Objectives

1 Practise 14 characters following the seven rules of stroke order

2 Learn to write Chinese numbers

1 Write the characters following the correct stroke order.

1 horizontal before vertical

shí *ten*

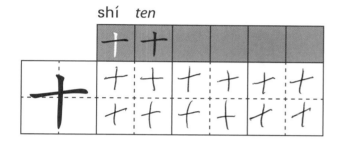

fēng *rich*

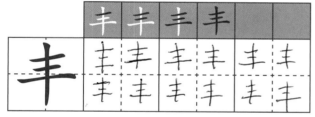

2 downward left before downward right

rén *people*

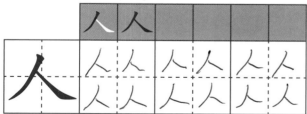

bā *eight*

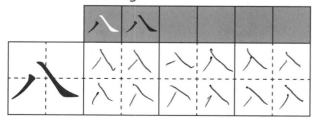

3 from left to right

chuān *river*

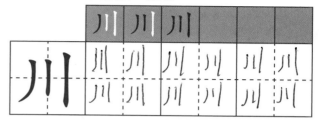

jiāng *big river*

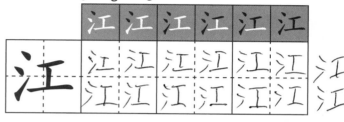

4 from top to bottom

sān *three*

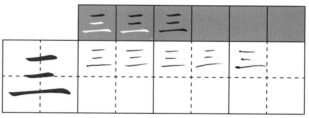

dīng *a Chinese surname*

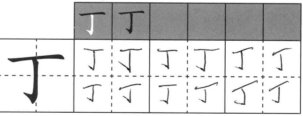

5 from outside to inside

yuè *moon, month*

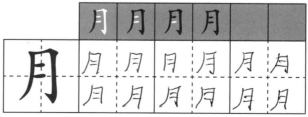

wèn *ask*

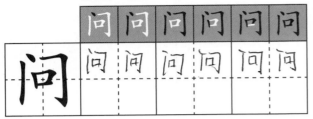

6 from outside to inside, then closing

huí *return*

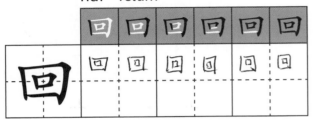

guó *country*

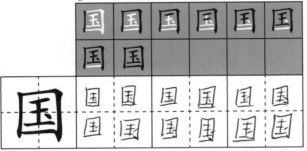

7 middle before two sides

xiǎo *small*

shuǐ *water*

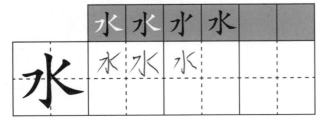

2 Write the Chinese numbers following the correct stroke order.

sì *four*

wǔ *five*

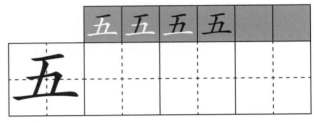

liù *six*

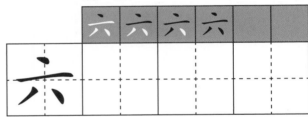

qī *seven*

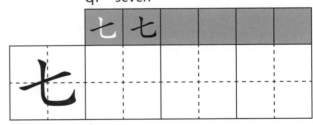

jiǔ *nine*

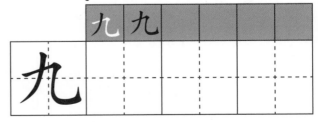

UNIT 1 Nǐ hǎo 你好! Hello!

LESSON 1

Objectives

1 **Vocabulary:** greetings and introductions

2 **Listening:** identify people's names and the four tones

3 **Pronunciation:** the four tones

4 **Grammar:** identify surnames and given names

5 **Conversation and listening:** understand greetings and introductions

Vocabulary

1 Match the words with the meanings.

1	名字	**a**	get to know
2	什么	**b**	glad, happy
3	认识	**c**	name
4	高兴	**d**	what
5	请问	**e**	may I ask, excuse me

Listening

2 Listen and check the names you hear.

1 □ **a** Dīng Huá 丁 华   □ **b** Dīng Huā 丁 花

2 □ **a** Wáng Yīng 王 英   □ **b** Wáng Yíng 王 莹

3 □ **a** Xiǎo Měi 小 美   □ **b** Xiǎo Méi 小 梅

4 □ **a** Mǎ Yīngwěi 马 英伟   □ **b** Mǎ Yíngwēi 马 莹薇

Pronunciation

3 Circle the correct tones for the characters.

1 我
wō   wó   wǒ   wò

2 什
shēn   shén   shěn   shèn

3 叫
jiāo   jiáo   jiǎo   jiào

4 名
mīng   míng   mǐng   mìng

5 姓
xīng   xíng   xǐng   xìng

Now write pinyin for the words.

6 你好 _____

7 请问 _____

8 什么 _____

9 名字 _____

10 你呢 _____

11 认识 _____

12 高兴 _____

13 对不起 _____

Grammar

4 Complete the sentences with the correct parts of people's names.

Wǒ shì Dīng Gāo' ān
1 我 是 丁 高安。
Wǒ xìng   míngzi jiào
我 姓 _____, 名字 叫_____。

Tā shì Wáng Yúnmíng
2 他 是 王 云明。
Tā xìng   míngzi jiào
他 姓 _____, 名字 叫_____。

Wǒ shì Lǐ Wěi
3 我 是 李 伟。
Wǒ xìng   míngzi jiào
我 姓 _____, 名字 叫_____。

Tā shì Sòng Yùxīng
4 她 是 宋 玉兴。
Tā xìng   míngzi jiào
她 姓 _____, 名字 叫_____。

Wǒ shì Lín Mǎkè
5 我 是 林 马克。
Wǒ xìng   míngzi jiào
我 姓 _____, 名字 叫_____。

Tā shì Liú Lì
6 她 是 刘 丽。
Tā xìng   tā jiào
她 姓 _____, 她 叫_____。

Tā shì Zhāng Wěi
7 他 是 张 伟。
Tā xìng   tā jiào
他 姓 _____, 他 叫_____。

Conversation and listening

5 Complete the conversation.

永民: 你好!

安娜: (1) _____!

永民: 请问, 你叫什么名字?

安娜: (2) _____ 安娜。你呢?

永民: 我叫永民, Kim Yeong-min。

　　　(3) _____ 你很高兴,

　　　安小姐。

安娜: (4) _____, 我姓Pollard。

6 Now listen and check the true statements.

☐ **5** Anna and Yeong-min are meeting for the first time.

☐ **6** Yeong-min's given name is Kim.

☐ **7** Yeong-min knows Anna's family name.

☐ **8** People often say 认识你很高兴 when they meet for the first time.

☐ **9** People often say 对不起 when they meet for the first time.

LESSON | 2

Objectives

1 **Reading:** recognize different kinds of name

2 **Writing:** make an introduction

3 **Writing:** introduce someone

4 **Grammar:** word order of Chinese sentences (I)

5 **Grammar:** verbs 姓 (xìng), 叫 (jiào) and 是 (shì)

6 **Grammar:** questions ending with 呢 (ne)

Reading

 1 Read Yeong-min's introduction and answer the questions.

大家好！

我叫 Kim Yeong-min，

中文名字是永民。

认识你们很高兴。

1 他姓什么?

_____

2 他叫什么名字?

_____

3 他的中文名字是什么?

_____

Writing

2 Read James' self-introduction and write a response.

你好! 我叫 James Whitbread，中文名字是詹姆斯。认识你很高兴。

_____

_____

_____

_____

_____

3 Write a few sentences about a friend using 姓, 叫 and 是.

Tā   Tā jiào
他 / 她 叫 _____

_____

_____

_____

_____

Grammar

4 Put the words in the correct order to make sentences.

jiào Wáng Yù wǒ
1 叫 / 王 玉 / 我 / 。

_____

Ānnà shì tā
2 安娜 / 是 / 她 / 。

_____

tā míngzi shénme jiào
3 他 / 名字 / 什么 / 叫 / ?

_____

Mǎkè shì de Zhōngwén míngzi
4 马克 / 是 / Mark 的 中文 名字 / 。

_____

shénme xìng nǐ
5 什么 / 姓 / 你 / ?

_____

xìng Wáng wǒ
6 姓 / 王 / 我 / 。

_____

5 Complete the conversations with the words in the box.

xìng	jiào	shì
姓	叫	是

王玉: 你们好, 我 (1) _____ 王,

(2) _____ 王玉, 认识你们很高

兴。

永民: 你们好! 我 (3) _____ Kim Yeong-

min, 中文名字 (4) _____ 永民。

你 (5) _____ 什么名字?

6 Match the questions with the answers.

Wǒ xìng Wáng nǐ ne
1 我 姓 王 , 你 呢? ____

Wǒ jiào Ānnà nǐ ne
2 我 叫 安娜, 你 呢? ____

Wǒ shì Shǐdìfū nǐ ne
3 我 是 史蒂夫, 你 呢? ____

Wǒ xìng nǐ ne
4 我 姓 Pollard, 你 呢? ____

Wǒ jiào nǐ ne
5 我 叫 Angela, 你 呢? ____

Wǒ shì nǐ ne
6 我 是 Steve, 你 呢? ____

Wǒ jiào Yǒngmín hěn gāoxìng rènshi nǐ
a 我 叫 永民 , 很 高兴 认识你。

Wǒ shì Wáng Yù
b 我 是 王 玉。

Wǒ xìng Liú
c 我 姓 刘。

Wǒ xìng
d 我 姓 Smith。

Wǒ shì
e 我 是 Michael。

Wǒ jiào
f 我 叫 Mark。

LESSON | 3

Objectives

1 **Conversation:** greet people for the first time
2 **Character reading:** recognize characters with the radicals 亻 and 女
3 **Character writing:** introduce people
4 **Vocabulary extension:** use different terms of address for people

Conversation

1 Put the sentences in the correct order to make a conversation.

a 我叫李华。认识你很高兴, 刘小姐。

b 我叫刘丽。你呢?

c 认识你很高兴。

d 你好! 请问, 你叫什么名字?

The correct order is _____.

Character reading

2 Match the radicals with the meanings.

1 亻   a woman

2 女   b man, person

Now match the words with the meanings.

3 她   c they

4 小姐   d Miss

5 伟   e she, her

6 他们   f great

Character writing

3 Make sentences using the words given.

1 她   小姐

_____

2 他   伟

_____

Vocabulary extension

4 Complete the sentences with the words in the box.

xiānsheng	xiǎojiě	nǚshì
先生	小姐	女士
tàitai	lǎoshī	tóngxué
太太	老师	同学

1 Ding Yuan is a teacher. You address him as _____.

2 Mark, Anna and Steve are schoolmates. They call each other _____.

3 You address Wang Yu, a young woman, as _____.

4 You meet Mr Wang. You greet and address him as _____.

5 You meet Mr Wang's wife on the street. You address her as _____.

6 You see a middle-aged man on campus and want to ask him the way to the student dormitory. You address him as _____.

7 You meet a young girl at the dining hall in a university. You call her _____.

8 You address a middle-aged woman at a conference as _____.

CHARACTER WRITING

Objectives

1 Practise six characters with the radicals 亻and 女
2 Learn to write seven common words for greetings and introductions

1 Write the characters with the radicals 亻and 女.

nǐmen   *you (plural)*

tā   *he, him*

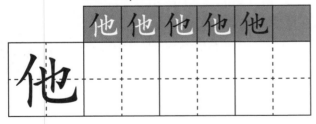

tā   *she, her*

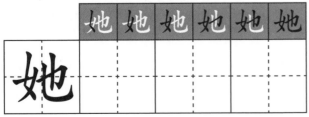

hǎo   *good*

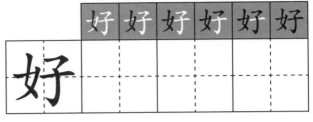

xìng   *surname, family name*

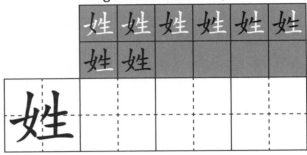

2 Write the words following the correct stroke order.

zhōngwén   *Chinese language*

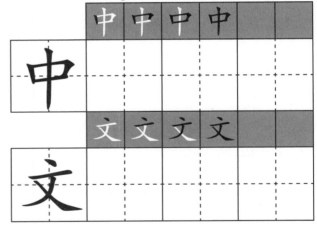

shénme   *what*

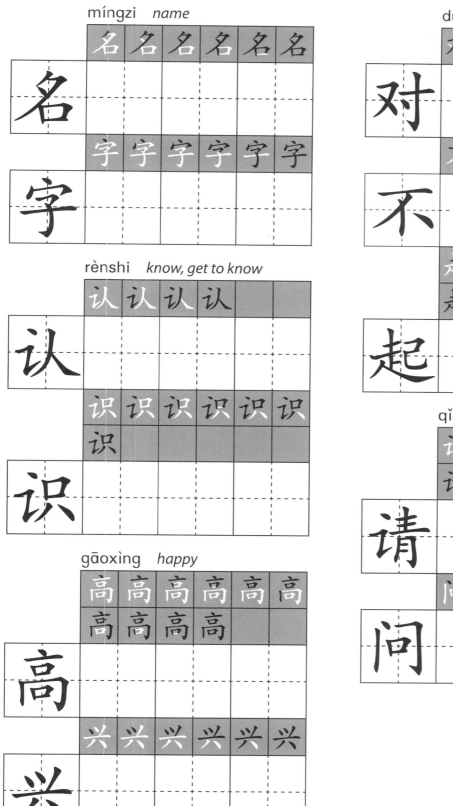

míngzi *name*

名	名	名	名	名	名
名					

字	字	字	字	字	字
字					

rènshi *know, get to know*

认	认	认	认		
认					

识	识	识	识	识	识
识					
识					

gāoxìng *happy*

高	高	高	高	高	高
高	高	高	高		
高					

兴	兴	兴	兴	兴	兴
兴					

duìbuqǐ *sorry*

对	对	对	对	对	
对					

不	不	不	不		
不					

起	起	起	起	起	起
起	起	起	起		
起					

qǐngwèn *may I ask*

请	请	请	请	请	请
请	请	请	请		
请					

问	问	问	问	问	问
问					

SELF-ASSESSMENT

Complete the checklist, using the criteria below.

1 = I need a lot of help to do this.

2 = I can do this with a little help.

3 = I can do this fairly well.

4 = I can do this very well.

5 = I can do this almost perfectly.

LANGUAGE SKILL	PROGRESS	YOUR SCORE
PRONUNCIATION	• I can identify the four tones. • I can say common Chinese surnames with the correct tones.	
VOCABULARY	• I know at least three Chinese surnames. • I know common words and expressions to greet people. • I know common words and phrases to introduce myself and other people.	
GRAMMAR	• I can identify the surname and given name of a Chinese person. • I understand basic word order in Chinese sentences. • I know how to use the verbs 姓, 叫 and 是 to talk about people's names. • I can ask questions about people's names using 什么. • I can ask follow-up questions with 呢.	
LISTENING	• I can identify people's names. • I can understand simple greetings and introductions.	
READING	• I know the meanings of the radicals 亻 and 女. • I can understand people's simple self-introductions.	
SPEAKING	• I can introduce myself and my friends. • I can ask for people's names.	
WRITING	• I can write six characters with the radicals 亻 and 女, and seven common words for greetings and introductions. • I can write a basic self-introduction.	

UNIT 2

Nǐ shì nǎli rén
你 是 哪里 人？
Where are you from?

LESSON | 1

Objectives

1 **Vocabulary:** words used to talk about nationalities

2 **Vocabulary:** country names

3 **Conversation and listening:** identify someone's nationality, where they come from and where they live

4 **Listening:** identify where people come from

5 **Pronunciation:** the four tones

6 **Grammar:** yes/no questions ending with 吗 (ma)

Vocabulary

1 Match the words with the meanings.

zhù zài
1 住 在　　　　　a no

nǎ guó
2 哪 国　　　　　b where

bù
3 不　　　　　　c people, man

rén
4 人　　　　　　d which country

ma
5 吗　　　　　　e live at/in

nǎli
6 哪里　　　　　f particle used to ask questions

2 Match the country names with the pictures.

Yīngguó
1 英国 _____

Jiānádà
5 加拿大 _____

Àodàlìyà
2 澳大利亚 _____

Zhōngguó
6 中国 _____

Měiguó
3 美国 _____

Fǎguó
7 法国 _____

Rìběn
4 日本 _____

Hánguó
8 韩国 _____

a

b

c

d

e

f

g

h

Conversation and listening

3 Listen to the conversation and complete the sentences.

> 马克： 你们好，我是马克。
>
> 你叫什么名字？
>
> 王 玉： 你好，我叫王玉。他是史蒂夫。
>
> 马克： 史蒂夫，你是哪国人？
>
> 史蒂夫： 我是英国人。你呢？
>
> 马克： 我是澳大利亚人。
>
> 史蒂夫： 你住在悉尼吗？
>
> 马克： 不，我住在北京。

1 史蒂夫是 ＿＿＿＿＿ 人。

2 马克是 ＿＿＿＿＿ 人。

3 马克住在 ＿＿＿＿＿ 。

Listening

4 Listen and check where the speakers are from.

1 □ **a** 韩国   □ **b** 日本

2 □ **a** 澳大利亚   □ **b** 加拿大

3 □ **a** 美国   □ **b** 英国

4 □ **a** 法国   □ **b** 中国

Pronunciation

5 Write pinyin for the words.

1 英国　　　　＿＿＿＿＿＿＿

2 伦敦　　　　＿＿＿＿＿＿＿

3 中国　　　　＿＿＿＿＿＿＿

4 北京　　　　＿＿＿＿＿＿＿

5 日本人　　　＿＿＿＿＿＿＿

6 澳大利亚人　＿＿＿＿＿＿＿

Grammar

6 Ask questions about the sentences using 吗.

1 ＿＿＿＿＿＿＿＿＿＿＿＿＿＿＿

　Wáng Yù shì Zhōngguórén
　王 玉 是 中国人。

2 ＿＿＿＿＿＿＿＿＿＿＿＿＿＿＿

　Wǒ zhù zài Běijīng
　我 住 在 北京。

3 ＿＿＿＿＿＿＿＿＿＿＿＿＿＿＿

　Yǒngmín shì Hánguórén
　永民 是 韩国人 。

4 ＿＿＿＿＿＿＿＿＿＿＿＿＿＿＿

　Wǒ bù rènshi Dīng Yuán
　我 不 认识 丁 原 。

5 ＿＿＿＿＿＿＿＿＿＿＿＿＿＿＿

　Mǎkè zhù zài Běijīng
　马克 住 在 北京。

LESSON | 2

Objectives

1 **Reading:** people's nationalities and where they live

2 **Reading:** identify a person's nationality

3 **Writing:** describe where someone comes from and where they live

4 **Grammar:** questions with an interrogative pronoun 哪里 (nǎli) / 哪 (nǎ)

5 **Grammar:** negative adverb 不 (bù)

6 **Conversation:** talk about nationalities and places

Reading

1 Read these people's name cards.

Peter Austin
美国人
住在澳大利亚悉尼

Kim Park
韩国人
住在中国北京

Jane Lee
加拿大人
住在日本

Now answer the questions.

1 Peter 姓什么?

_____

2 Peter 是澳大利亚人吗?

_____

3 Park 是中国人吗?

_____

4 Park 住在哪里?

_____

5 Jane 是哪国人?

_____

6 Jane 住在日本吗?

_____

2 Read the introduction and answer the questions.

> Jackie Chan 是好莱坞明星。但是他不是美国人,他是中国人。

1 Jackie Chan 是明星吗?

_____

2 他是哪国人?

_____

Writing

3 Write three sentences to introduce Steve.

_____

_____

_____

_____

Grammar

4 Ask questions about the underlined parts of the sentences using 哪里 or 哪国.

Wǒ zhù zài Zhōngguó
1 我 住 在 中国。

_____

Tā zhù zài Lúndūn
2 他 住 在 伦敦。

_____

Shǐdìfū shì Yīngguórén
3 史蒂夫 是 英国人。

_____

Tā shì Rìběnrén
4 她 是 日本人。

_____

5 Put 不 in the correct places in the sentences.

Lúndūn zài Měiguó
1 伦敦 在 美国。

_____

Tā jiào Mǎ Lì
2 她 叫 马 丽。

_____

Wǒ rènshi Ānnà
3 我 认识 安娜。

_____

Now answer the questions using your own information, and using 不 when necessary.

Nǐ zhù zài Běijīng ma
4 你 住 在 北京 吗？

_____

Nǐ shì Yīngguórén ma
5 你 是 英国人 吗？

_____

Conversation

6 Complete the conversations using the correct words in the brackets.

Wáng Yù shì   nǎ guó zhù zài
1 A: 王 玉 是 _____ (哪国 / 住 在)
rén
人？

Tā shì   Zhōngguórén
B: 她 是 _____ (中国人 /
Zhōngguó
中国)。

Nǐ rènshi Mǎkè   ma ne
2 A: 你 认识 马克 _____ (吗 / 呢)？
Wǒ   bù bù shì rènshi Mǎkè
B: 我 _____ (不 / 不是) 认识马克。

Tāmen shì   nǎ guó rén
3 A: 他们 是 _____ (哪 国 人 /
Měiguó
美国)？

Duìbuqǐ Nǐ hǎo wǒ bù
B: _____ (对不起 / 你 好)，我 不
zhīdào
知道 。

LESSON | 3

Objectives

1 **Conversation:** exchange personal information about where you live

2 **Character reading:** recognize characters with the radicals 口 and 日

3 **Character writing:** ask questions about where people come from

4 **Vocabulary extension:** countries and places

Conversation

1 Complete the conversation with the words in the box.

nǎ guó rén 哪 国 人	zhù zài 住 在	Lúndūn 伦敦
nǐ hǎo 你 好	Yīngguórén 英国人	Běijīng 北京

丁云:　你好! 我叫丁云。我是中国人,

　　　　住在 (1) _____。

史蒂夫:　丁云, (2) _____! 我叫史蒂夫。

丁云:　请问, 你 是 (3) _____?

史蒂夫:　我是 (4) _____。

丁云:　你住在 (5) _____ 吗?

史蒂夫:　不, 我 (6) _____ 北京。

Character reading

2 Match the radicals with the meanings.

1 口　　　　a sun

2 日　　　　b mouth

Now match the words with the meanings.

3 呢　　　　c bright

4 是　　　　d be

5 哪　　　　e particle used to ask questions

6 明　　　　f which

Character writing

3 Make questions using the words given.

1 日本人　　吗

　　_____

2 是　　　　哪里

　　_____

Vocabulary extension

4 Complete the table with the countries in the box.

	Yīngguó		Fǎguó		Déguó
a	英国	f	法国	k	德国
	Měiguó		Jiānádà		Mòxīgē
b	美国	g	加拿大	l	墨西哥
	Nánfēi		Kěnníyà		Āijí
c	南非	h	肯尼亚	m	埃及
	Zhōngguó		Rìběn		Hánguó
d	中国	i	日本	n	韩国
	Xīnjiāpō		Tàiguó		Yìndù
e	新加坡	j	泰国	o	印度

Continent	Countries
Asia	
Europe	
America	
Africa	

CHARACTER WRITING

Objectives

1 Practise five characters with the radicals 口 and 日

2 Learn to write nine common words for greetings, nationalities and where people live

1 Write the characters with the radicals 口 and 日.

jiào   *be called*

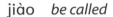

ma   *particle used to ask questions*

míngxīng   *celebrity*

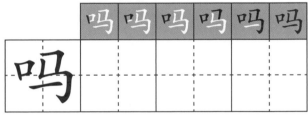

shì   *be*

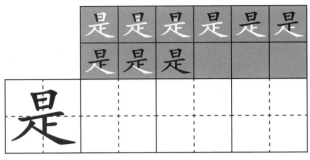

2 Write the words following the correct stroke order.

zǎoshang   *morning*

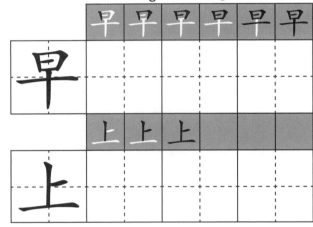

bù   *no*

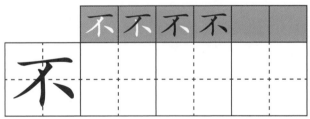

dàn   *but*

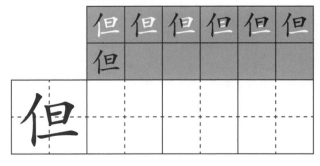

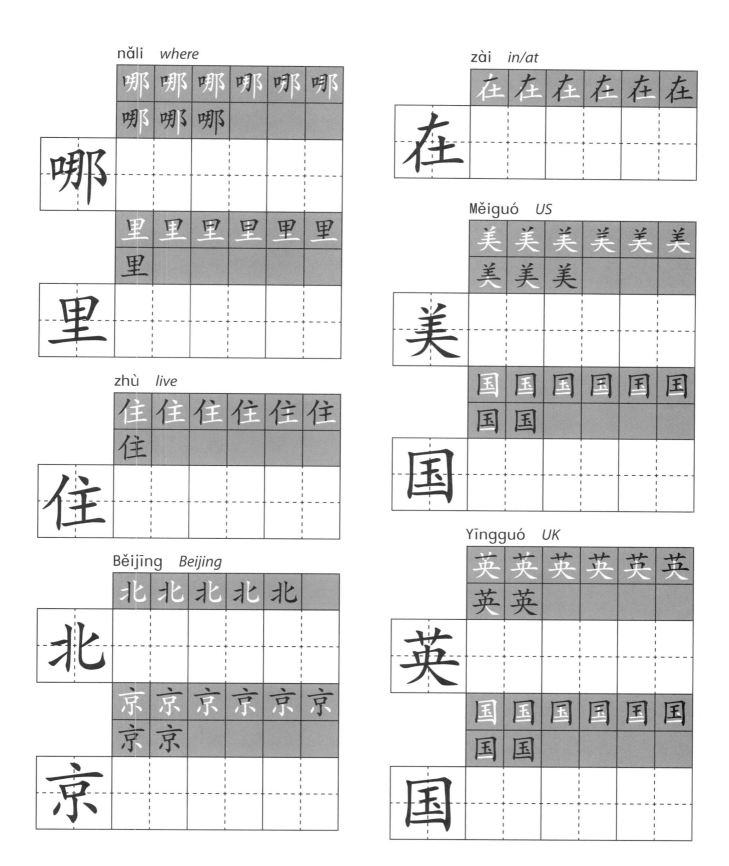

nǎli *where*

哪 哪 哪 哪 哪 哪
哪 哪 哪

哪

里 里 里 里 里 里
里

里

zhù *live*

住 住 住 住 住 住
住

住

Běijīng *Beijing*

北 北 北 北 北
京 京 京 京 京 京
京 京

北

京

zài *in/at*

在 在 在 在 在 在

在

Měiguó *US*

美 美 美 美 美 美
美 美 美

美

国 国 国 国 国 国
国 国

国

Yīngguó *UK*

英 英 英 英 英 英
英 英

英

国 国 国 国 国 国
国 国

国

SELF-ASSESSMENT

Complete the checklist, using the criteria below.

1 = I need a lot of help to do this.

2 = I can do this with a little help.

3 = I can do this fairly well.

4 = I can do this really well.

5 = I can do this almost perfectly.

LANGUAGE SKILL	PROGRESS	YOUR SCORE
PRONUNCIATION	• I can identify the four tones. • I can say country names with the correct tones.	
VOCABULARY	• I can name at least six countries. • I can name at least four cities. • I know common words and phrases to tell people my nationality and where I live. • I know how to introduce someone's nationality, where they are from, and where they live.	
GRAMMAR	• I can ask yes/no questions with 吗. • I can ask questions about places and nationalities using 哪里 and 哪. • I can make negative sentences with 不.	
LISTENING	• I can identify people's nationality. • I can understand people saying where they are from. • I can understand people saying where they live.	
READING	• I know the meanings of the radicals 口 and 日. • I can recognize characters to understand people's self-introductions, including nationality and where they live.	
SPEAKING	• I can introduce my nationality and other people's. • I can ask people where they are from and where they live.	
WRITING	• I can write five characters with the radicals 口 and 日, and nine common words for nationalities and where people live. • I can write a short passage introducing someone's nationality and where they live.	

UNIT 3

Nǐ zuò shénme gōngzuò
你做什么工作?
What do you do?

LESSON 1

Objectives

1 **Vocabulary:** occupations and family members

2 **Vocabulary:** words used to talk about occupations

3 **Conversation and listening:** identify information about family members and their occupations

4 **Reading and writing:** identify information about family members and write about one's own family

5 **Pronunciation:** the finals: a, e, i

Vocabulary

1 Circle the odd word out.

	bàba 1 爸爸	jìzhě 记者	māma 妈妈
	gōngzuò 2 工作	dìdi 弟弟	jiějie 姐姐
	yīshēng 3 医生	hùshi 护士	yīyuàn 医院
	míngxīng 4 明星	xuésheng 学生	lǎoshī 老师

2 Translate the words into Chinese.

1 do _____

2 work, job _____

3 what _____

4 where _____

Conversation and listening

3 Complete the conversation with the words in the box.

xuésheng 学生	jiějie 姐姐	yīyuàn 医院
nǎli 哪里	zhàopiàn 照片	gōngzuò 工作

马克: 你好, 刘丽。

刘丽: 你好, 马克。这是我家的

(1) _____。

马克: 刘丽, 她是你姐姐吗?

刘丽: 是, 她是我 (2) _____。

马克: 她住在 (3) _____?

刘丽: 她住在悉尼。

马克: 我弟弟也住在悉尼。你姐姐在哪里

(4) _____?

刘丽: 她在 (5) _____ 工作, 她是医生。
你弟弟呢?

马克: 他是 (6) _____。

Now listen to the conversation and check the true statements.

☐ 7 刘丽和马克都是医生。

☐ 8 马克的弟弟和刘丽的姐姐都住在悉尼。

☐ 9 刘丽的姐姐在医院工作。

☐ 10 马克的弟弟不是学生。

Reading and writing

4 Read the excerpt from Mark's letter about his family and check the true statements.

> 我爸爸是医生，我妈妈也是医生，他们都在医院工作。我妹妹是记者，我弟弟是学生。

☐ 1 马克的爸爸在医院工作。
☐ 2 马克的妈妈不是医生。
☐ 3 马克的妹妹是学生。
☐ 4 马克的弟弟不是记者。

Now write three sentences about your own family.

5 _____

6 _____

7 _____

Pronunciation

5 Write pinyin for the words.

1 他 _____

2 爸爸 _____

3 妈妈 _____

4 哪 _____

5 加拿大 _____

6 法国 _____

7 也 _____

8 这 _____

9 和 _____

10 哥哥 _____

11 记者 _____

12 呢 _____

13 一 _____

14 弟弟 _____

15 是 _____

16 名字 _____

17 哪里 _____

18 医生 _____

LESSON | 2

Objectives

1 **Reading:** understand an introduction to someone's family

2 **Writing:** introduce someone's family

3 **Grammar:** adverbs 也 (yě) and 都 (dōu)

4 **Grammar:** word order of Chinese sentences (II)

5 **Grammar:** pronouns as modifiers + 的 (de)

Reading

1 Read Ding Yun's introduction and answer the questions.

我叫丁云，我是学校的老师。

学生都叫我丁老师。

我哥哥也是老师，他在英国。

我姐姐在法国，她是记者。

1 丁云做什么工作？

_____

2 他在哪里工作？

_____

3 他哥哥住在哪里？他姐姐呢？

_____

Writing

2 Write four sentences about your best friend's family.

_____

_____

_____

_____

Grammar

3 Put 也 and 都 in the correct places in the sentences.

Mǎkè hé Yǒngmín bù rènshi Ānnà
1 马克 和 永民 不认识 安娜。

Tā hěn gāoxìng   wǒ hěn gāoxìng
2 他 很 高兴， 我 很 高兴。

Wǒ bàba māma shì yīshēng
3 我 爸爸 妈妈 是 医生 。

Wǒ dìdi zhù zài Běijīng
4 我 弟弟 住 在 北京。

Tā xìng Dīng   wǒ xìng Dīng
5 他 姓 丁，我 姓 丁。

Wǒ shì xuésheng   wǒ mèimei shì xuésheng
6 我 是 学生 ， 我 妹妹 是 学生。

Tāmen shì xuéxiào de lǎoshī
7 他们 是 学校 的 老师。

Shǐdìfū shì Yīngguórén
8 史蒂夫 是 英国人。

Now check the correct sentences.

Tā jiào Mǎkè   tā bàba dōu jiào Mǎkè
☐ 9 他 叫 马克，他 爸爸 都 叫 马克。

Wáng Yù hé Wáng Yún dōu xìng Wáng
☐ 10 王 玉 和 王 云 都 姓 王 。

Yīshēng hé hùshi yě zài yīyuàn gōngzuò
☐ 11 医生 和 护士 也 在 医院 工作 。

Wǒ gēge hé dìdi dōu bù zhù zài Běijīng
☐ 12 我 哥哥 和 弟弟 都 不 住 在 北京。

4 Put the words in the correct order to make sentences.

zài yīyuàn   gōngzuò   tā
1 在 医院 / 工作 / 她 /。

_____

Yǒngmín   Hánguórén   shì   yě
2 永民 / 韩国人 / 是 / 也 /。

_____

Běijīng   Wáng Yù   zhù zài
3 北京 / 王 玉 / 住 在 /。

_____

Zhōngwén míngzi   de   Ānnà   shì
4 中文 名字 / 的 / 安娜 / 是 / Anna /。

_____

dōu   xuésheng   shì   wǒmen
5 都 / 学生 / 是 / 我们 /。

_____

Xīní   zhù zài   bù   Mǎkè
6 悉尼 / 住 在 / 不 / 马克 /。

_____

yě   Běijīng   wǒ   zhù zài
7 也 / 北京 / 我 / 住 在 /。

_____

zài xuéxiào   gōngzuò   tā gēge
8 在 学校 / 工作 / 她 哥哥 /。

_____

Now write two sentences about yourself using 也 and 都.

9 _____

10 _____

5 Put the words in the correct order to make noun phrases.

gōngzuò   yīshēng   de
1 工作 / 医生 / 的

_____

xuésheng   wǒ   de
2 学生 / 我 / 的

_____

zhàopiàn   Ānnà   jiā   de
3 照片 / 安娜 家 / 的

_____

hùshi   yīyuàn   de
4 护士 / 医院 / 的

_____

gōngzuò   bàba   de
5 工作 / 爸爸 / 的

_____

zhàopiàn   jiějie   de
6 照片 / 姐姐 / 的

_____

Now check the correct sentences.

Wǒ māma zài yīyuàn gōngzuò
☐ 7 我 妈妈 在 医院 工作。

Wǒ míngzi shì Wáng Yù
☐ 8 我 名字 是 王 玉。

Zhè shì wǒ de jiā de zhàopiàn
☐ 9 这 是 我 的 家 的 照片。

Wǒ jiějie shì yīyuàn de hùshi
☐ 10 我 姐姐 是 医院 的 护士。

LESSON │ 3

Objectives

1 **Conversation:** ask questions about people's families
2 **Character reading:** recognize characters with the radicals 宀 and 阝
3 **Character writing:** write about occupations
4 **Vocabulary extension:** occupations

Conversation

1 Write questions for the answers to complete the conversation.

A: _____?

B: 我叫刘瑜。

A: _____?

B: 我爸爸叫刘伟。

A: _____?

B: 他是中国人。

A: _____?

B: 我妈妈也是中国人。

A: _____?

B: 他们都住在北京。

Character reading

2 Match the radicals with the meanings.

1 宀   a city

2 阝   b roof

Now match the words with the meanings.

3 安   c that

4 那   d both, all

5 家   e family, home

6 都   f safe and stable

Character writing

3 Make sentences using the words given.

1 都   医生

_____

2 哪里   工作

_____

Vocabulary extension

4 Complete the table with the words in the box.

dǎoyóu 导游	lùshī 律师	chúshī 厨师
mìshū 秘书	gōngchéngshī 工程师	fúwùyuán 服务员
hùshi 护士	lǐfàshī 理发师	xiūlǐgōng 修理工

工作地点 (place)	职业 (job)
室内 (indoors)	
室外 (outdoors)	

CHARACTER WRITING

Objectives

1 Practise five characters with the radicals 宀 and 阝

2 Learn to write ten common words for family members and jobs

1 Write the characters with the radicals 宀 and 阝.

jiā *family, home*

家	家	家	家	家	家
家	家	家	家		

家

ān *safe and stable*

安	安	安	安	安	安

安

zì *character*

字	字	字	字	字	字

字

dōu *both, all*

都	都	都	都	都	都
都	都	都	都		

都

nà *that*

那	那	那	那	那	那

那

2 Write the words following the correct stroke order.

bà *father*

爸	爸	爸	爸	爸	爸
爸	爸				

爸

mā *mother*

妈	妈	妈	妈	妈	妈

妈

jiě *elder sister*

姐	姐	姐	姐	姐	姐
姐	姐				

姐

mèi *younger sister*

妹 妹 妹 妹 妹 妹
妹 妹

妹

gē *elder brother*

哥 哥 哥 哥 哥 哥
哥 哥 哥 哥

哥

dì *younger brother*

弟 弟 弟 弟 弟 弟
弟

弟

gōngzuò *work, job*

工 工 工

工

作 作 作 作 作 作
作

作

yīshēng *doctor*

医 医 医 医 医 医
医

医

生 生 生 生 生

生

lǎoshī *teacher*

老 老 老 老 老 老

老

师 师 师 师 师 师

师

xuésheng *student*

学 学 学 学 学 学
学 学

学

生 生 生 生 生

生

SELF-ASSESSMENT

Complete the checklist, using the criteria below.

1 = I need a lot of help to do this.

2 = I can do this with a little help.

3 = I can do this fairly well.

4 = I can do this really well.

5 = I can do this almost perfectly.

LANGUAGE SKILL	PROGRESS	YOUR SCORE
PRONUNCIATION	• I can identify and say words with the finals "a", "e" and "i".	
VOCABULARY	• I can name at least four jobs. • I know common words and phrases to introduce my family and other people.	
GRAMMAR	• I can make sentences with the correct word order. • I can use the adverb 也 to express "also". • I can use the adverb 都 to express "both" or "all". • I can make sentences with pronouns as modifiers and 的. • I can make noun phrases with the correct word order.	
LISTENING	• I can identify people's occupations. • I can understand people introducing their family members.	
READING	• I know the meanings of the radicals 宀 and 阝. • I can recognize characters used to describe a photo of someone's family and their occupations.	
SPEAKING	• I can introduce my occupation and other people's occupations. • I can introduce my family members and other people. • I can ask someone about their job and family.	
WRITING	• I can write five characters with the radicals 宀 and 阝, and ten common words for family members and jobs. • I can write a short passage introducing someone and their family members' occupations. • I can fill in a simple student registration form for a course.	

UNIT 4

Tā zhēn gāo
他 真 高!
He's so tall!

LESSON | 1

Objectives

1 **Vocabulary:** words used to describe people

2 **Vocabulary:** adjectives used to describe appearance

3 **Conversation and listening:** talk about favourite people and their appearance

4 **Pronunciation:** the finals: ao, uei (ui), en

Vocabulary

1 Write eight words used to describe people with the characters in the box.

nián 年	piāo 漂	zhī 知	ài 爱
míng 名	dào 道	huan 欢	xìng 姓
xǐ 喜	qīng 轻	míng 明	dà 大
xīng 星	kě 可	duō 多	liàng 亮

1 _____   5 _____

2 _____   6 _____

3 _____   7 _____

4 _____   8 _____

2 Use as many adjectives as possible to describe the people in the pictures.

ǎi **a** 矮	niánqīng **d** 年轻	lǎo **g** 老
gāo **b** 高	kě'ài **e** 可爱	shuài **h** 帅
kù **c** 酷	piàoliang **f** 漂亮	

a

1 _____

b

2 _____

Conversation and listening

3 Listen to the conversation and check the true statements.

> 永民：他是谁？
>
> 安娜：他是刘丽的哥哥。
>
> 永民：他叫什么名字？
>
> 安娜：他叫刘明。
>
> 永民：他多大？
>
> 安娜：二十八岁。
>
> 永民：他做什么工作？
>
> 安娜：他是记者。
>
> 永民：真酷！

☐ **1** 他是刘丽的哥哥。

☐ **2** 刘丽的哥哥姓刘明。

☐ **3** 他二十八岁。

☐ **4** 他是老师。

☐ **5** 他不在学校工作。

Pronunciation

4 Write pinyin for the words.

1 老 _____

2 早上 _____

3 对不起 _____

4 最高 _____

5 真 _____

6 很好 _____

7 熊猫 _____

8 国籍 _____

9 姚明 _____

10 澳大利亚人 _____

Now make sentences using the words given.

11 老师　　　早上

_____

12 姚明　　　国籍

_____

13 熊猫　　　真

_____

14 我　　　　最喜欢

_____

LESSON | 2

Objectives

1 **Reading:** find basic information about someone in their personal profile

2 **Writing:** create a personal profile for yourself

3 **Grammar:** interrogative pronoun 谁 (shéi) and ask about age using 多大 (duō dà)

4 **Grammar:** numbers in Chinese

5 **Grammar:** 真 (zhēn) / 很 (hěn) + adjective

Reading

1 Read Anna's Sina profile and check the true statements.

☐ 1 安娜十九岁。

☐ 2 她的出生地不是伦敦。

☐ 3 安娜不喜欢篮球。

☐ 4 王玉是安娜的同学。

Writing

2 Answer the questions.

1 你多大?

_____

2 你是哪国人?

_____

3 你最喜欢的同学是谁?

_____

4 你最喜欢的演员是谁?

_____

Now design a Sina profile for yourself.

_____

_____

_____

_____

新浪博客   博客首页   微博：最火交流工具 看明星动态   [登录] [注册]   [✍发博文 ▼] [_____] [博文 ▼] [搜索]

首页 | 博文 | 图片 | 关于我

我的资料

[播客] [微博]
進入我的空间

[加好友] [发纸条]
[写留言] [加关注]

博客等级：**22**
博客积分：806
博客访问：5,631,496

我的档案

姓名：　　安娜　　　　　年龄：　十八岁
　　　　　Niǔyuē

出生地：　纽约 (New York)　国籍：　美国

电子邮箱：anna123@DC.com

最喜欢的运动：篮球——很酷！

最喜欢的演员：Nicole Kidman——很漂亮！

最喜欢的同学：王玉——很可爱！

Grammar

3 Write questions for the answers using 谁 or 多大.

Wǒ shíbā suì
1 我 十八 岁。

_____

Tā shì Liú Dàwěi
2 他 是 刘 大伟。

_____

Wǒ jiějie sānshí suì
3 我 姐姐 三十 岁。

_____

Wǒ de tóngxué shíjiǔ suì
4 我 的 同学 十九 岁。

_____

Tā hé Wáng xiānsheng zài dàxué gōngzuò
5 他 和 王 先生 在 大学 工作。

_____

4 Complete the table with the numbers in Chinese.

Numbers	Chinese	Numbers	Chinese
11	十一	24	二十四
12	十二	38	三十八
13		45	
14	十四	47	
15	十五	52	
16		56	
17	十七	63	
18		67	六十七
19	十九	71	
21	二十一	90	九十
22		99	

Now listen and order the numbers in the sequence you hear them.

☐ **a** 19   ☐ **e** 24

☐ **b** 34   ☐ **f** 95

☐ **c** 18   ☐ **g** 80

☐ **d** 71   ☐ **h** 27

5 Put 真 or 很 in the correct places in the sentences.

Nǐ māma niánqīng
1 你 妈妈 年轻!

Tā kù
2 他 酷!

Wáng lǎoshī shuài
3 王 老师 帅!

Mǎkè xǐhuan Běijīng
4 马克 喜欢 北京。

Xióngmāo kě'ài
5 熊猫 可爱。

Tā gāo
6 她 高!

Now check the correct sentences.

Shǐ yīshēng hěn niánqīng
☐ **7** 史 医生 很 年轻。

Tā xǐhuan hěn lánqiú
☐ **8** 他 喜欢 很 篮球。

Zuò jìzhě zhēn kù
☐ **9** 做 记者 真 酷!

Tā gēge zhēn gāo
☐ **10** 他 哥哥 真 高!

Tā jiějie shì hěn hǎo
☐ **11** 她 姐姐 是 很 好。

Yáo Míng bù zhēn shuài
☐ **12** 姚 明 不 真 帅。

LESSON | 3

Objectives

1 **Conversation:** talk about favourite people
2 **Character reading:** recognize characters with the radicals 土 and 氵
3 **Character writing:** describe where people live
4 **Vocabulary extension:** expressions used to describe people

Conversation

1 Complete the conversation with the words in the box.

yùndòngyuán	lánqiú	hěn
运动员	篮球	很
xiànzài	**kù**	**ma**
现在	酷	吗

A: 你喜欢 (1) _____ 吗?

B: 我 (2) _____ 喜欢篮球。

A: 你喜欢的篮球 (3) _____ 是谁?

B: 我最喜欢姚明。他很 (4) _____。

A: 他住在上海 (5) _____?

B: 不, 他 (6) _____ 住在美国。

Character reading

2 Match the radicals with the meanings.

1 土 a earth

2 氵 b water

Now match the words with the meanings.

3 演员   c Australia

4 澳大利亚   d Hollywood

5 现在   e actor, actress

6 好莱坞   f now

Character writing

3 Make sentences using the words given.

1 住在   澳大利亚

_____

2 现在   好莱坞

_____

Vocabulary extension

4 Match the sentences with the people.

Tā gèzi gāo duǎn tóufa   hěn shuài
1 他 个子 高， 短 头发， 很 帅。____

Tā gèzi ǎi   hěn piàoliang
2 她 个子 矮， 很 漂亮。   ____

Tā bù niánqīng duǎn tóufa
3 他 不 年轻， 短 头发。   ____

CHARACTER WRITING

Objectives

1 Practise six characters with the radicals 土 and 氵

2 Learn to write seven common words for describing people's appearance

1 **Write the words containing the radicals 土 and 氵.**

chūshēngdì   *place of birth*

出 出 出 出 出

出

生 生 生 生 生

生

地 地 地 地 地 地

地

Shànghǎi   *Shanghai*

上 上 上

上

海 海 海 海 海 海
海 海 海 海

海

piàoliang   *pretty*

漂 漂 漂 漂 漂 漂
漂 漂 漂 漂 漂 漂
漂 漂

漂

亮 亮 亮 亮 亮 亮
亮 亮 亮

亮

zài   *at, in*

在 在 在 在 在 在

在

Fǎguó   *France*

法 法 法 法 法 法
法 法

法

国 国 国 国 国 国
国 国

国

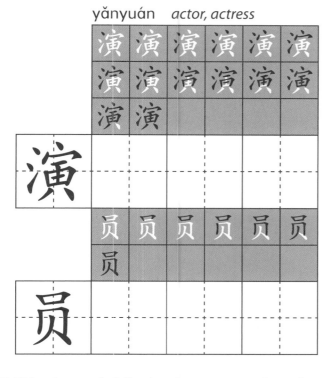

yǎnyuán *actor, actress*

演	演	演	演	演	演
演	演	演	演	演	演
演	演				

演

| 员 | 员 | 员 | 员 | 员 | 员 |
| 员 | | | | | |

员

shuài *handsome*

| 帅 | 帅 | 帅 | 帅 | 帅 | |

帅

kù *cool*

酷	酷	酷	酷	酷	酷
酷	酷	酷	酷	酷	酷
酷	酷				

酷

2 Write the words following the correct stroke order.

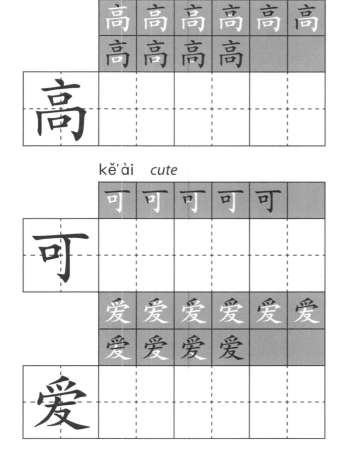

gāo *tall*

| 高 | 高 | 高 | 高 | 高 | 高 |
| 高 | 高 | 高 | 高 | | |

高

kě'ài *cute*

| 可 | 可 | 可 | 可 | 可 | |

可

| 爱 | 爱 | 爱 | 爱 | 爱 | 爱 |
| 爱 | 爱 | 爱 | 爱 | | |

爱

niánqīng *young*

| 年 | 年 | 年 | 年 | 年 | 年 |

年

| 轻 | 轻 | 轻 | 轻 | 轻 | 轻 |
| 轻 | 轻 | 轻 | | | |

轻

ǎi *short*

矮	矮	矮	矮	矮	矮
矮	矮	矮	矮	矮	矮
矮					

矮

SELF-ASSESSMENT

Complete the checklist, using the criteria below.

1 = I need a lot of help to do this.   4 = I can do this very well.

2 = I can do this with a little help.   5 = I can do this almost perfectly.

3 = I can do this fairly well.

LANGUAGE SKILL	PROGRESS	YOUR SCORE
PRONUNCIATION	• I can identify and say words with the finals "ao", "uei" and "en".	
VOCABULARY	• I can say at least six adjectives about people's appearance. • I know common words and phrases to describe people's appearance. • I can describe my favourite people and animals.	
GRAMMAR	• I can ask questions with the interrogative pronoun 谁. • I can say the numbers from 11 to 99 in Chinese. • I can ask about age using 多大. • I can use the adverbs 真 and 很 with adjectives to indicate a high degree.	
LISTENING	• I can understand simple descriptions of people's appearance.	
READING	• I know the meanings of the radicals 土 and 讠. • I can read basic information about people in their personal profiles.	
SPEAKING	• I can talk about people's appearance. • I can ask who someone is and how old they are.	
WRITING	• I can write six characters with the radicals 土 and 讠, and seven common words for describing people's appearance. • I can create a simple personal profile.	

UNIT 5

Zhè shì wǒ de diànhuà hàomǎ

这是我的电话号码。
Here's my phone number.

LESSON | 1

Objectives

1 **Vocabulary:** addresses and contact numbers

2 **Vocabulary:** words used to talk about addresses and contact numbers

3 **Conversation and listening:** identify contact numbers, postal and email addresses

4 **Pronunciation:** the tones of 不 (bù)

Vocabulary

1 Listen and check the phrases or sentences you hear.

1　□ **a** 北京路10号

　　□ **b** 大学路10号

2　□ **a** 邮箱地址

　　□ **b** 电子邮箱

3　□ **a** 你的电话号码

　　□ **b** 你的手机号码

4　□ **a** 我的电话号码是55546998。

　　□ **b** 我的电话号码是46998555。

2 Write pinyin for the words.

1　电话　　＿＿＿＿＿＿＿＿

2　手机　　＿＿＿＿＿＿＿＿

3　号码　　＿＿＿＿＿＿＿＿

4　多少　　＿＿＿＿＿＿＿＿

5　地址　　＿＿＿＿＿＿＿＿

6　什么　　＿＿＿＿＿＿＿＿

7　路　　　＿＿＿＿＿＿＿＿

8　哪里　　＿＿＿＿＿＿＿＿

Now write sentences using the words given.

9　电话　　　多少

　　＿＿＿＿＿＿＿＿＿＿＿＿＿＿＿＿

10　地址　　　什么

　　＿＿＿＿＿＿＿＿＿＿＿＿＿＿＿＿

11　你　　　　哪里

　　＿＿＿＿＿＿＿＿＿＿＿＿＿＿＿＿

12　我　　　　电子邮箱

　　＿＿＿＿＿＿＿＿＿＿＿＿＿＿＿＿

Conversation and listening

3 Complete the conversation with the sentences in the box.

David: 你的电话号码是 30541296 吗?

Angela: _____

David: 你的手机号码是多少?

Angela: _____

David: 你住在哪里?

Angela: _____

David: 你的电子邮箱是什么?

Angela: _____

---

1 我住在大学路 23 号。

2 我的手机号码是 16628958763。

3 是，这是我家的电话号码。

4 angela@DC.com

Now listen and check your answers.

Pronunciation

4 Listen and write the correct tones for 不.

Wǒ bu xǐhuan lánqiú
1 我 不 喜欢 篮球。

Zhè bu shì wǒ de shǒujī hàomǎ
2 这 不 是 我 的 手机 号码。

Tāmen bu gāoxìng
3 他们 不 高兴。

Ānnà bu zài yīyuàn gōngzuò
4 安娜 不 在 医院 工作。

Xióngmāo bu kě'ài
5 熊猫 不 可爱。

Ānnà bu xìng Ān
6 安娜 不 姓 安。

Now write pinyin for the words.

7 不帅 _____

8 不酷 _____

9 不叫 _____

10 不认识 _____

11 不老 _____

12 不年轻 _____

13 不好 _____

14 不知道 _____

15 不漂亮 _____

16 不工作 _____

LESSON | 2

Objectives

1 **Vocabulary:** text message terms

2 **Reading:** understand a simple text message about contact information

3 **Writing:** give your contact details

4 **Grammar:** question word 多少 (duōshao)

5 **Grammar:** word order of Chinese addresses

6 **Pronunciation:** the pronunciation of the number "1"

✉ 新短信

永民，你好!
你的新地址是什么?
这是我的新电话号码,
你可以给我打电话。
发件人: 王玉 11872356725

选项　　　　　退出

Vocabulary

1 Match the words with the meanings.

fājiànrén
1 发件人   **a** send

shōujiànxiāng
2 收件箱   **b** new message

shōudào
3 收到   **c** exit, go back

fāsòng
4 发送   **d** sender

tuìchū
5 退出   **e** receive

xīn duǎnxìn
6 新 短信   **f** inbox

Reading

2 Read the text message and answer the questions.

1 王玉知道永民住在哪里吗?

_____

2 永民可以给王玉打电话吗?

_____

3 王玉的电话号码是多少?

_____

Writing

3 Write a message to your friend telling him/her your address and home phone number.

_____

_____

_____

Grammar

4 Write questions for the answers using 多少.

Wǒ de fángjiān hào shì
1 我 的 房间 号 是 3608。

_____

Tā de diànhuà hàomǎ shì
2 他 的 电话 号码 是 86752345。

_____

Wáng Yù zhù zài Dàxué Lù hào
3 王 玉 住 在 大学 路 24 号。

_____

Shǐdìfū de shǒujī hàomǎ shì
4 史蒂夫 的 手机 号码 是 12081345761。

_____

Now answer the questions with your own information.

Nǐ de diànhuà hàomǎ shì duōshao
5 你 的 电话 号码 是 多少？

_____

Nǐ zhù zài nǎli
6 你 住 在 哪里？

_____

Nǐ de fángjiān hào shì duōshao
7 你 的 房间 号 是 多少？

_____

5 Put the words in the correct order to make addresses.

hào fángjiān hào Dàxué Lù
1 1319 号 房间 / 23 号 / 大学 路 /

Dàxuéshēng gōngyù
大学生 公寓

_____

Gōngyuán Lù Běijīng hào Zhōngguó
2 公园 路 / 北京 / 26 号 / 中国

_____

hào xīn Shànghǎi gōngyù Shànghǎi Lù
3 75 号 / 新 上海 公寓 / 上海 路

_____

hào Běijīng Lù
4 38 号 / 北京 路

_____

Dàxué Lù Lúndūn gōngyù hào
5 大学 路 / 伦敦 公寓 / 15 号

_____

xīn Dàxuéshēng gōngyù hào fángjiān
6 新 大学生 公寓 / 709 号 房间

_____

6 Write pinyin for the numbers.

1 我的电话号码是 8311650179。

_____

2 我住在北京路 1 号。

_____

3 大学生公寓 119 号房间

_____

4 我哥哥 31 岁。

_____

5 王玉的新家在公园路 12 号。

_____

6 一二三四五

_____

7 她的手机号码是 10922103318。

_____

8 他住在 21 号房间。

_____

9 今天是三月二号，星期一。

_____

10 11 个房间

_____

LESSON | 3

Objectives

1 **Writing:** ask for addresses and contact numbers
2 **Character reading:** recognize characters with the radicals 讠 and 辶
3 **Character writing:** write about contact numbers
4 **Vocabulary extension:** words and word order of addresses

Writing

1 Write a text message to your friend asking for his/her home address, email address and home phone number.

_____

_____

_____

Character reading

2 Match the radicals with the meanings.

1 讠   **a** walk

2 辶   **b** speech

Now match the words with the meanings.

3 认识   **c** this

4 谁   **d** telephone

5 这   **e** who

6 电话   **f** know

Character writing

3 Make sentences using the words given.

1 知道   号码

_____

2 这   电话

_____

Vocabulary extension

4 Write the addresses on the envelopes in Chinese.

1 Wang Na, Room 103, Student Apartment
No. 28 Garden Street, Beijing, China

2 Liu Yu, No. 1 Beijing Street, Xinrong District
Xianghua City, Sichuan Province, China

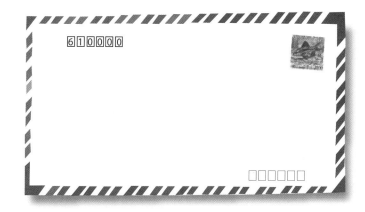

CHARACTER WRITING

Objectives

1 Practise six characters with the radicals 讠 and 辶

2 Learn to write seven common words for addresses and contact numbers

1 Write the words containing the radicals 讠 and 辶.

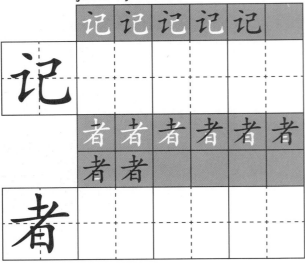

jìzhě   *journalist*

shéi   *who*

zhè   *this*

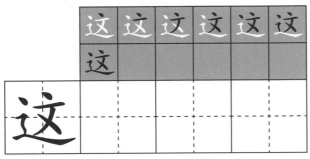

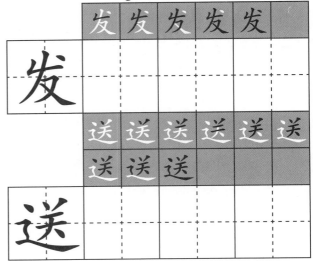

fāsòng   *send*

tuìchū   *exit, go back*

2 Write the words following the correct stroke order.

diànhuà   *telephone*

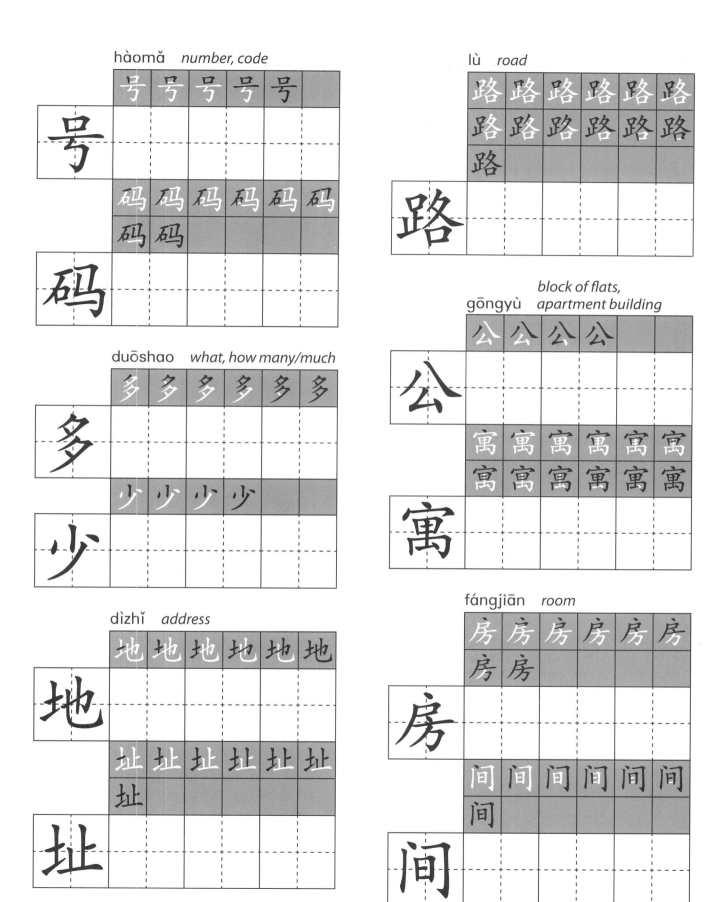

hàomǎ *number, code*

号	号	号	号	号	

号

码	码	码	码	码	码
码	码				

码

duōshao *what, how many/much*

多	多	多	多	多	多

多

少	少	少	少		

少

dìzhǐ *address*

地	地	地	地	地	地

地

址	址	址	址	址	址
址					

址

lù *road*

路	路	路	路	路	路
路	路	路	路	路	路
路					

路

gōngyù *block of flats, apartment building*

公	公	公	公		

公

寓	寓	寓	寓	寓	寓
寓	寓	寓	寓	寓	寓

寓

fángjiān *room*

房	房	房	房	房	房
房	房				

房

间	间	间	间	间	
间					

间

SELF-ASSESSMENT

Complete the checklist, using the criteria below.

1 = I need a lot of help to do this.　　4 = I can do this very well.

2 = I can do this with a little help.　　5 = I can do this almost perfectly.

3 = I can do this fairly well.

LANGUAGE SKILL	PROGRESS	YOUR SCORE
PRONUNCIATION	• I can identify and say the word 不 in different phrases with the correct tones. • I can pronounce the number "1" in different expressions correctly.	
VOCABULARY	• I can express addresses and contact numbers. • I know common text message terms.	
GRAMMAR	• I can ask questions about contact numbers and addresses using 多少. • I know the correct word order to give Chinese addresses.	
LISTENING	• I can identify contact numbers, postal addresses and email addresses.	
READING	• I know the meanings of the radicals 讠 and 辶. • I can recognize characters to understand simple text messages about addresses and contact numbers.	
SPEAKING	• I can ask for contact numbers and addresses. • I can say contact numbers and addresses.	
WRITING	• I can write six characters with the radicals 讠 and 辶, and seven common words for addresses and contact numbers. • I can write simple messages about contact numbers.	

UNIT 6 今天 几 号?
Jīntiān   jǐ   hào

What's the date today?

LESSON | 1

Objectives

1 **Vocabulary:** months

2 **Vocabulary:** days of the week

3 **Vocabulary:** days of the week, months and dates

4 **Conversation and listening:** talk about birthdays and make invitations

5 **Pronunciation:** the initials: j, q, x

Vocabulary

1 Match the Chinese months with the English ones.

1	二月	**a**	January
2	五月	**b**	February
3	一月	**c**	March
4	七月	**d**	May
5	九月	**e**	June
6	十二月	**f**	July
7	三月	**g**	August
8	六月	**h**	September
9	十月	**i**	October
10	八月	**j**	December

2 Put the days of the week in the correct order.

Xīngqīwǔ
a 星期五

Xīngqī'èr
e 星期二

Xīngqīsān
b 星期三

Xīngqīliù
f 星期六

Xīngqīyī
c 星期一

Xīngqīsì
g 星期四

Xīngqītiān
d 星期天

The correct order is _____.

3 Match the questions with the answers.

Jīntiān jǐ hào
1 今天 几 号? _____

Jīntiān xīngqījǐ
2 今天 星期几? _____

Xīngqīliù shì jǐ hào
3 星期六 是 几 号? _____

Jiǔyuè yī hào shì Xīngqīwǔ ma
4 九月 一 号 是 星期五 吗? _____

Xīngqītiān shì èrshíqī hào ma
5 星期天 是 二十七 号 吗? _____

Jīntiān Xīngqī'èr
a 今天 星期二。

Shì   Jiǔyuè yī hào shì Xīngqīwǔ
b 是, 九月 一 号 是 星期五。

Jīntiān Sānyuè èr hào
c 今天 三月 二 号。

Xīngqīliù shì Qīyuè wǔ hào
d 星期六是 七月 五 号。

Bù shì   Xīngqītiān shì èrshíliù hào
e 不是, 星期天 是 二十六 号。

Conversation and listening

4 Put the sentences in the correct order to make a conversation.

a 你的生日是几月几号?

b 我十八岁。

c 我的生日是十月四号。

d 我请你去"北京厨房"吃饭, 怎么样?

e 谢谢。

f 王娜, 你多大?

g 太好了, 谢谢! 那里的中餐很好吃。

h 是今天吗? 生日快乐!

The correct order is _____.

23 Now listen to the conversation and check the true statements.

□ **1** 王娜的生日是十月四号。

□ **2** 今天不是十月四号。

□ **3** 王娜二十岁。

□ **4** 她喜欢去"北京厨房"。

Pronunciation

5 Write pinyin for the words.

1 星期几 _____

2 家 _____

3 发件人 _____

4 叫 _____

5 今天 _____

6 北京 _____

7 见 _____

8 房间 _____

9 请 _____

10 去 _____

11 九十七 _____

12 小姐 _____

13 谢谢 _____

14 新 _____

15 姓 _____

16 学生 _____

LESSON | 2

Objectives

1 **Vocabulary:** everyday activities

2 **Reading:** understand activities in a weekly planner

3 **Writing:** create a weekly planner

4 **Grammar:** months and dates

5 **Grammar:** sentences without verbs

6 **Grammar:** make invitations using 请 (qǐng)

Vocabulary

1 Match the phrases with the meanings.

pàiduì
1 派对   a meet up

jiànmiàn
2 见面   b read a book

chīfàn
3 吃饭   c learn Chinese

kàn shū
4 看 书   d have a meal

qù yīyuàn
5 去 医院   e play basketball

xué Zhōngwén
6 学 中文   f party

shàngbān
7 上班   g go to hospital

dǎ lánqiú
8 打 篮球   h go to work

Reading

2 Read Yeong-min's weekly planner and answer the questions.

1 永民几号去医院?

_____

2 永民星期几学中文?

_____

3 妈妈的生日派对是几月几号?

_____

三月七日 — 九日

	9:00 – 12:00	12:00 – 3:00	3:00 – 6:00	6:00 – 9:00
星期 一	学中文	跟史蒂夫见面	上班	请王玉吃饭
星期 二		上班	打篮球	妈妈的生日派对
星期 三	学中文		去医院	跟马克去吃中餐

Writing

3 Write your own weekly planner.

	9:00 – 12:00	12:00 – 3:00	3:00 – 6:00	6:00 – 9:00
星期 一				
星期 二				
星期 三				

Grammar

4 Put the dates in order from the earliest to the latest.

a 三月十号   d 六月十九号

b 八月二十号   e 三月二十八号

c 八月四号   f 四月三十号

The correct order is _____.

Now write six sentences about your activities over the next three days.

1 _____

2 _____

3 _____

4 _____

5 _____

6 _____

5 Check the correct sentences.

　　　　Tā mèimei hěn kě'ài
☐ 1 她 妹妹 很 可爱！

　　　　Jīntiān shì shíliù hào
☐ 2 今天 是 十六 号。

　　　　Wáng yīshēng shì sānshí suì
☐ 3 王 医生 是 三十 岁。

　　　　Jīntiān Xīngqīyī
☐ 4 今天 星期一。

　　　　Wǒ bù gāoxìng
☐ 5 我 不 高兴。

Now write the sentences in Chinese.

6 Today is Friday.

_____

7 His mother is 40 years old.

_____

8 Yao Ming is really cool!

_____

9 Her brother is very tall.

_____

10 What date is today?

_____

6 Make sentences using 请 and the words given.

　　Wáng Yù　　　　qù pàiduì　　　　wǒ
1 王 玉　　　　去 派对　　　　我

_____

　　Mǎkè　　　　lǎoshī　　　　chīfàn
2 马克　　　　老师　　　　吃饭

_____

　　Ānnà　　　　qù tā jiā　　　　Yǒngmín
3 安娜　　　　去 她 家　　　　永民

_____

　　Shǐdìfū　　　　chī Zhōngcān　　　　Wáng Yù
4 史蒂夫　　　　吃 中餐　　　　王 玉

_____

Now write two sentences involving yourself using 请.

5 _____

6 _____

LESSON | 3

Objectives

1 **Vocabulary:** public holidays in China
2 **Character reading:** recognize characters with the radicals 月 and 扌
3 **Character writing:** write about everyday activities
4 **Vocabulary extension:** days and dates

Vocabulary

1 Complete the table with the Chinese public holidays in the box.

a	Yuándàn 元旦	New Year	一月一日
b	Chúxī 除夕	Chinese New Year's Eve	二月十三日
c	Chūnjié 春节	Spring Festival	二月
d	Qīngmíngjié 清明节	Tomb Sweeping Festival	四月五日
e	Láodòngjié 劳动节	Labour Day	五月一日
f	Duānwǔjié 端午节	Dragon Boat Festival	六月十六日
g	Zhōngqiūjié 中秋节	Mid-Autumn Festival	九月二十二日
h	Guóqìngjié 国庆节	National Day	十月一日

月份	节日	月份	节日
January		July	
February		August	
March		September	
April		October	
May		November	
June		December	

Character reading

2 Match the radicals with the meanings.

1 月   a hand

2 扌   b moon

Now match the words with the meanings.

3 二月   c Friday

4 星期五   d nurse

5 打篮球   e February

6 护士   f play basketball

Character writing

3 Make sentences using the words given.

1 星期五   打篮球

_____

2 给   打电话

_____

Vocabulary extension

4 Complete the table with the appropriate days and dates.

Last	Present	Next
qùnián 去年		
	zhège yuè 这个 月	
		xiàge xīngqī 下个 星期
	jīntiān 今天	
Shíyuè 十月		

CHARACTER WRITING

Objectives

1 Practise four characters with the radicals 月 and 扌

2 Learn to write nine common words for dates and daily activities

1 Write the words containing the radicals 月 and 扌.

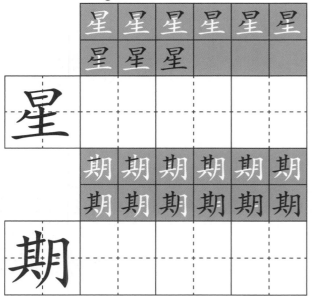

yuè *month*

月	月	月	月		
月					

xīngqī *week*

星	星	星	星	星	星
星	星	星			
星					

期	期	期	期	期	期
期	期	期	期	期	期
期					

dǎ *play*

打	打	打	打	打	
打					

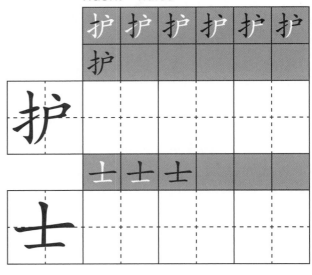

hùshi *nurse*

护	护	护	护	护	护
护					
护					

士	士	士			
士					

2 Write the words following the correct stroke order.

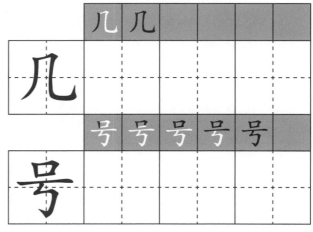

jīntiān *today*

今	今	今	今		
今					
天	天	天	天		
天					

jǐhào *what date*

几	几			
几				
号	号	号	号	号
号				

chīfàn *have a meal*

吃 吃 吃 吃 吃 吃
吃

饭 饭 饭 饭 饭 饭
饭
饭

qù *go*

去 去 去 去 去
去

xué *study, learn*

学 学 学 学 学 学
学 学
学

zuò *do*

做 做 做 做 做 做
做 做 做 做 做
做

jiànmiàn *meet up*

见 见 见 见
见

面 面 面 面 面 面
面 面 面
面

kànshū *read a book*

看 看 看 看 看 看
看 看 看
看

书 书 书 书
书

shàngbān *go to work*

上 上 上
上

班 班 班 班 班 班
班 班 班 班
班

SELF-ASSESSMENT

Complete the checklist, using the criteria below.

1 = I need a lot of help to do this.
2 = I can do this with a little help.
3 = I can do this fairly well.

4 = I can do this very well.
5 = I can do this almost perfectly.

LANGUAGE SKILL	PROGRESS	YOUR SCORE
PRONUNCIATION	• I can identify and say words with the initials "j", "q" and "x".	
VOCABULARY	• I know the words for months and days of the week. • I know how to express dates. • I know common words and phrases to make invitations. • I know five words for everyday activities. • I can name five public holidays in China.	
GRAMMAR	• I can express dates and months. • I can make sentences without verbs to express age, dates, days of the week and time. • I can make invitations using 请.	
LISTENING	• I can identify days of the week, months and dates. • I can understand people talking about what day or date something will happen. • I can understand people's birth dates. • I can understand people making invitations.	
READING	• I know the meanings of the radicals 月 and 扌. • I can understand activities in a weekly planner.	
SPEAKING	• I can ask for and say dates and days. • I can say my date of birth. • I can make simple invitations.	
WRITING	• I can write four characters with the radicals 月 and 扌, and nine common words for dates and daily activities. • I can complete a weekly planner.	

UNIT 7

Bā diǎn jiàn

八点见！

See you at eight!

LESSON | 1

Objectives

1 **Vocabulary:** the time

2 **Vocabulary:** words used to talk about social plans

3 **Conversation and listening:** plan a social activity

4 **Pronunciation:** difference between "u" and "ü"

5 **Grammar:** express future tense using the verb 要 (yào)

Vocabulary

1 Number the times in the order you hear them.

☐ **a** 5:20
☐ **b** 1:25
☐ **c** 10:40
☐ **d** 3:00
☐ **e** 2:15
☐ **f** 6:30
☐ **g** 11:55
☐ **h** 12:45

2 Match the words with the meanings.

shíjiān 1 时间	**a** weekend
zhōumò 2 周末	**b** time
kāishǐ 3 开始	**c** tomorrow
jìhuà 4 计划	**d** start
míngtiān 5 明天	**e** plan

Conversation and listening

3 Complete the conversation with the words and phrases in the box.

wǎnshang 晚上	*ménkǒu* 门口	*tài hǎo le* 太好了
jǐdiǎn 几点	*yǒu shíjiān* 有时间	*kàn diànyǐng* 看电影

永民： 星期一去 (1) _____, 好吗?

安娜： 星期一是几号?

永民： 星期一是二十号。

安娜： 好, 我 (2) _____。我们看什么电影?

永民： 你喜欢美国电影吗?

安娜： 我很喜欢。

永民： (3) _____。我们看 New York 1982, 怎么样?

安娜： 好。(4) _____?

永民： (5) _____ 九点半, 可以吗?

安娜： 没问题。星期一九点在电影院 (6) _____ 见。

26 Now listen to the conversation and check the true statements.

☐ 7 星期一是二十二号。

☐ 8 永民和安娜星期一看电影。

☐ 9 安娜喜欢美国电影。

☐ 10 电影的名字叫New York 1983。

☐ 11 电影九点三十分开始。

Pronunciation

4 Check the correct pinyin for the words.

1 退出   ☐ **a** tuìchū   ☐ **b** tuìqū

2 看书   ☐ **a** kàn xū   ☐ **b** kàn shū

3 动物   ☐ **a** dòngwù   ☐ **b** dòngyù

4 护士   ☐ **a** hùshi   ☐ **b** qùshi

5 公寓   ☐ **a** gōngxù   ☐ **b** gōngyù

6 很酷   ☐ **a** hěn kù   ☐ **b** hěn gù

7 厨房   ☐ **a** chúfáng   ☐ **b** qúfáng

8 不好   ☐ **a** xù hǎo   ☐ **b** bù hǎo

9 马路   ☐ **a** mǎlù   ☐ **b** mǎlù

10 五天   ☐ **a** wǔ tiān   ☐ **b** yǔ tiān

27 Now listen and check your answers.

Grammar

5 Put 要 in the correct places in the sentences.

Tā qù Lúndūn
1 他 去 伦敦。

Tāmen wǎnshang xué Yīngyǔ
2 他们 晚上 学 英语。

Zhōumò wǒ kàn yéye nǎinai
3 周末 我 看 爷爷 奶奶。

Wǒ xiàwǔ gēn péngyou dǎ lánqiú
4 我 下午 跟 朋友 打 篮球。

Míngtiān wǒ gěi tā xiě diànzǐ yóujiàn
5 明天 我 给 她 写 电子 邮件。

Now complete the conversations using 要 and the words in brackets.

Nǐ Xīngqīliù zuò shénme
6 A: 你 星期六 做 什么？

B: _____。

xué Zhōngwén
（学 中文 ）

Nǐ xiàwǔ qù nǎli
7 A: 你 下午 去 哪里？

B: _____。

yīyuàn
（医院）

Nǐ wǎnshang gēn shéi chī Zhōngcān
8 A: 你 晚上 跟 谁 吃 中餐？

B: _____。

mèimei
（妹妹 ）

Nǐ zhège zhōumò yǒu shénme jìhuà
9 A: 你 这个 周末 有 什么 计划？

B: _____。

tīng yīnyuèhuì
（听 音乐会）

LESSON | 2

Objectives

1 **Vocabulary:** time, family members and everyday activities

2 **Grammar:** adverbial expressions of time

3 **Grammar:** different ways of telling the time

4 **Reading:** understand activities in a weekend planner

5 **Writing:** create a weekend planner and describe future actions using 要

Vocabulary

1 Circle the odd word out.

1 a 跑步 pǎobù   b 听 音乐 tīng yīnyuè   c 打 篮球 dǎ lánqiú

2 a 记者 jìzhě   b 爷爷 yéye   c 奶奶 nǎinai

3 a 博客 bókè   b 电影 diànyǐng   c 电子 邮件 diànzǐ yóujiàn

4 a 上午 shàngwǔ   b 晚上 wǎnshang   c 明天 míngtiān

5 a 到 dào   b 一起 yìqǐ   c 见 jiàn

6 a 唱歌 chànggē   b 中文 Zhōngwén   c 英语 Yīngyǔ

7 a 晚饭 wǎnfàn   b 中餐 Zhōngcān   c 日本菜 Rìběncài

8 a 写 xiě   b 听 tīng   c 酷 kù

Now make sentences using the words given.

9 上午   打篮球

_____

10 一起   吃日本菜

_____

Grammar

2 Circle the time expressions in the sentences.

Wǒ Xīngqī' èr wǎnshang kàn diànyǐng
1 我 星期二 晚上 看 电影。

Nǐmen míngtiān zuò shénme
2 你们 明天 做 什么？

Xiàwǔ sì diǎn nǐ yào kàn yīshēng
3 下午 四 点 你 要 看 医生。

Now write the sentences in Chinese.

4 We'll meet at the entrance of the university at 10:30 tomorrow morning.

_____

5 I exercise on Wednesday afternoon.

_____

6 I will go to the concert with friends on Sunday.

_____

3 Write two ways of telling each of these times.

Time	Expression 1	Expression 2
7:30		
10:15		
9:45		
12:30		
6:15		
2:45		

Reading

4 Read Anna's weekend planner and check the true statements.

☐ **1** 安娜星期六上午不在家。

☐ **2** 她星期六到"妈妈厨房"吃饭。

☐ **3** 她星期六下午打篮球。

☐ **4** 她星期六晚上跟马克听音乐会。

☐ **5** 马克的生日是星期六。

☐ **6** 安娜星期日中午在家。

☐ **7** 电影两点一刻开始。

☐ **8** 安娜星期日晚上请马克吃日本菜。

周末计划簿		星期六
要做的事	上午	在家写博客
	中午	12:45 在"妈妈厨房"吃中餐
	下午	3:30 打篮球
	晚上	8:00 跟王玉听音乐会
备忘录	给马克写生日卡	
		星期日
要做的事	上午	7:00 跟史蒂夫跑步
	中午	12:00 在家吃饭
	下午	2:15 跟朋友看电影
	晚上	6:30 马克的生日，请他吃韩国菜
备忘录	给老师写电子邮件	

Writing

5 Write a weekend planner for yourself.

周末计划簿		星期六
要做的事	上午	
	中午	
	下午	
	晚上	
备忘录		
		星期日
要做的事	上午	
	中午	
	下午	
	晚上	
备忘录		

Now write six sentences about your activities in the weekend planner using 要.

1 _____

2 _____

3 _____

4 _____

5 _____

6 _____

LESSON | 3

Objectives

1 **Reading:** understand people's weekly plan
2 **Character reading:** recognize characters with the radicals 门 and 𧾷
3 **Character writing:** plan social activities
4 **Vocabulary extension:** leisure activities

Reading

1 Read Steve's online dialogue with his friends and complete the invitation message at the end.

> Steve
>
> 你们星期几有时间？我们一起吃饭好吗？
>
> Anna
>
> 我星期二晚上打篮球。星期三学唱歌。
>
> Yeong-min
>
> 我星期一学中文，星期六听音乐会。我星期三、星期五有时间。
>
> Wang Yu
>
> 星期四是妈妈的生日，我要在家吃饭。星期天跟朋友看电影。
>
> Steve
>
> 星期 _____ 大家都有时间，我们一起吃晚饭吧。

Character reading

2 Match the radicals with the meanings.

1 门   **a** foot

2 𧾷   **b** gate

Now match the words with the meanings.

3 路   **c** entrance, doorway

4 时间   **d** jog

5 跑步   **e** time

6 门口   **f** road

Character writing

3 Make sentences using the words given.

1 时间   跑步

_____

2 门口   见

_____

Vocabulary extension

4 Write four sentences using the words in the box.

yóuyǒng	mǎi dōngxi
游泳	买 东西
kàn diànshì	kàn bǐsài
看 电视	看 比赛

1 _____

2 _____

3 _____

4 _____

CHARACTER WRITING

Objectives

1   Practise four characters with the radicals 门 and 𧾷

2   Learn to write ten common words for time expressions and daily activities

1 Write the words containing the radicals 门 and 𧾷.

pǎobù   *jog*

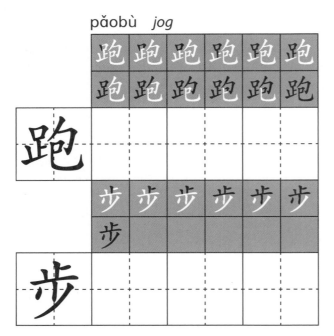

shíjiān   *time*

mén   *door*

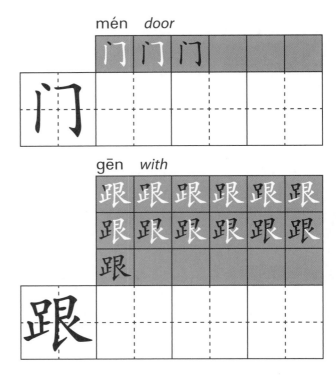

2 Write the words following the correct stroke order.

fēn   *minute*

kè   *quarter (of an hour)*

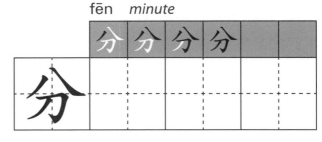

bàn   *half (an hour)*

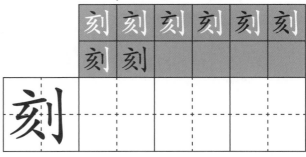

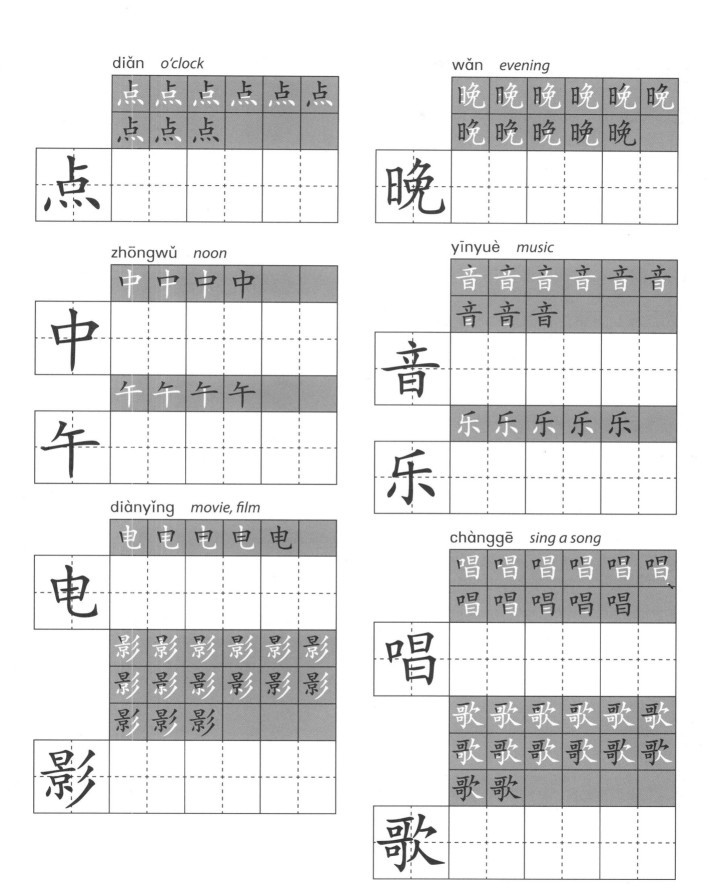

diǎn *o'clock*

点

wǎn *evening*

晚

zhōngwǔ *noon*

中
午

yīnyuè *music*

音
乐

diànyǐng *movie, film*

电
影

chànggē *sing a song*

唱
歌

SELF-ASSESSMENT

Complete the checklist, using the criteria below.

1 = I need a lot of help to do this.   4 = I can do this very well.

2 = I can do this with a little help.   5 = I can do this almost perfectly.

3 = I can do this fairly well.

LANGUAGE SKILL	PROGRESS	YOUR SCORE
PRONUNCIATION	• I can identify and say words with the finals "u" and "ü".	
VOCABULARY	• I know the words and expressions to say the time. • I know common words and expressions to plan a social activity.	
GRAMMAR	• I can make sentences with adverbial expressions of time. • I can express the time in two different ways. • I can express future actions using the verb 要.	
LISTENING	• I can identify the time. • I can understand people planning simple social activities.	
READING	• I know the meanings of the radicals 门 and 足. • I can understand characters used to tell the time. • I can understand activities in a weekend planner.	
SPEAKING	• I can ask for and tell the time. • I can make simple plans for social activities.	
WRITING	• I can write four characters with the radicals 门 and 足, and ten common words for time expressions and daily activities. • I can create a weekend planner.	

UNIT 8

Duōshǎo qián?

多少 钱?

How much is it?

LESSON | 1

Objectives

1 **Vocabulary:** prices
2 **Vocabulary:** colours and clothes
3 **Vocabulary:** colours of things
4 **Conversation and listening:** buy clothes
5 **Conversation:** negotiate a price
6 **Pronunciation:** the tones of —

Vocabulary

1 Write the prices in Chinese characters.

1 ¥154 _____

2 ¥91 _____

3 ¥898 _____

2 Number the clothes items in the order you hear them.

hóngsè de xié
□ a 红色 的 鞋

hēisè de máoyī
□ b 黑色 的 毛衣

báisè de tīxù
□ c 白色 的 T恤

lùsè de qúnzi
□ d 绿色 的 裙子

lánsè de kùzi
□ e 蓝色 的 裤子

huángsè de dàyī
□ f 黄色 的 大衣

3 Match the colours with the things.

hēisè
1 黑色

a

báisè
2 白色

b

lùsè
3 绿色

c

huángsè
4 黄色

d

hóngsè
5 红色

lánsè
6 蓝色

e

Conversation and listening

4 Complete the conversation with the words in the box.

duìbuqǐ	dàyī	le	shìshi
对不起	大衣	了	试试
zěnmeyàng	bùcuò	tiáo	xǐhuan
怎么样	不错	条	喜欢

售货员：这件 (1) _____ 怎么样？

王玉：太大 (2) _____！

售货员：这 (3) _____ 裤子呢？

王玉：我不 (4) _____ 黑色。

售货员：这件毛衣 (5) _____？

王玉：(6) _____。我可以

(7) _____ 吗？

售货员：(8) _____，不可以。

王玉：那我不买了。

31 Now listen to the conversation and check the true statements.

☐ **9** 这件大衣太大。

☐ **10** 王玉喜欢黑色。

☐ **11** 这件毛衣好看。

☐ **12** 王玉可以试毛衣。

☐ **13** 王玉没有买毛衣。

Conversation

5 Put the sentences in the correct order to make a conversation.

a
Xièxie
谢谢。

b
Sānbǎi jiǔshí kuài
三百 九十 块。

c
Duìbuqǐ   sānbǎi kuài zhège jiàqian hěn
对不起，三百 块 这个 价钱 很
piányi
便宜。

d
Liǎngbǎi kuài zěnmeyàng
两百 块 怎么样？

e
Zhè tiáo hóngsè de qúnzi hěn hǎokàn
这 条 红色 的裙子 很 好看！

Duōshao qián
多少 钱？

f
Tài guì le   Piányi yīdiǎnr ba
太 贵 了。便宜 一点儿 吧。

g
Hǎo ba   Gěi nǐ qián
好吧。给你 钱。

h
Sānbǎi kuài bā
三百 块 吧。

The correct order is _____.

Pronunciation

6 Write pinyin for the phrases, including the correct tone for 一 in spoken Chinese.

1 一起 _____

2 一百块 _____

3 一双鞋 _____

4 一件大衣 _____

LESSON | 2

Objectives

1 **Vocabulary:** shopping places in the city
2 **Reading:** understand descriptions of what people bought
3 **Writing:** write a blog entry about things you bought
4 **Grammar:** measure words
5 **Grammar:** numerals 二 (èr) and 两 (liǎng)
6 **Grammar:** express past tense using 了 (le)

Vocabulary

1 Match the words with the meanings.

1 购物中心   **a** bookshop

2 服装市场   **b** supermarket

3 书店   **c** clothes market

4 超市   **d** shopping centre

Reading

2 Read Wang Yu's blog.

Now check the true statements.

☐ 1 高云是王玉的好朋友。

☐ 2 高云在书店工作了四年。

☐ 3 王玉星期六在服装市场买了一件大衣。

☐ 4 大衣不便宜，但是很漂亮。

☐ 5 王玉有三十一件T恤。

☐ 6 白色的T恤最多。

☐ 7 王玉没有蓝色的T恤。

☐ 8 王玉不喜欢红色。

Writing

3 Write a blog entry about the things you bought recently. Use the blog from Activity 2 to help you.

_____

_____

_____

_____

_____

_____

_____

_____

_____

_____

Grammar

4 Complete the phrases with the words in the box.

tiáo	shuāng	jiàn	gè
条	双	件	个

1　yī　一 _____ kùzi 裤子

2　yī　一 _____ shǒu 手

3　yī　一 _____ tīxù T恤

4　yī　一 _____ máojīn 毛巾

5　yī　一 _____ píngguǒ 苹果

6　yī　一 _____ lù 路

7　yī　一 _____ qúnzi 裙子

8　yī　一 _____ yǎnjing 眼睛

9　yī　一 _____ yuè 月

10　yī　一 _____ péngyou 朋友

11　yī　一 _____ dàyī 大衣

12　yī　一 _____ xié 鞋

13　yī　一 _____ rén 人

14　yī　一 _____ máoyī 毛衣

15　yī　一 _____ xīngqī 星期

5 Write the words in Chinese using 二 or 两.

1　Tuesday _____

2　two people _____

3　February _____

4　twelve students _____

5　2 December _____

6　¥20 _____

7　2:10 pm _____

8　325 _____

6 Put 了 in the correct places in the sentences.

Shàng gè zhōumò wǒ kàn yéye nǎinai
1　上 个 周末 我 看 爷爷 奶奶。

Wǒ zài Měiguó rènshi hěn duō péngyou
2　我 在 美国 认识 很 多 朋友。

Tā Xīngqīsān qù Shànghǎi
3　她 星期三 去 上海。

Wǒ zài zhèli zhù sān nián
4　我 在 这里 住 三 年。

Tā bàba zhīdào zhè jiàn shì
5　他 爸爸 知道 这 件 事。

Now write the sentences in Chinese.

6　They have gone to Shanghai.

_____

7　I asked him where he lives.

_____

8　Anna bought two pairs of shoes.

_____

9　Mark arrived at the university at 8 o'clock.

_____

LESSON | 3

Objectives

1 **Listening:** understand an introduction from a shop assistant

2 **Character reading:** recognize characters with the radicals 衤 and 贝

3 **Character writing:** write about shopping

4 **Vocabulary extension:** items of clothing

Listening

1 Listen to Ma Xiaoyu's introduction and answer the questions.

大家好！我是马小玉。我是中国人，住在北京。我在超市工作。这个超市不大，也不太有名，但是有很多英国、美国和日本的东西，价钱也不贵。周末很多人来这里买东西。请你们也来这里买东西吧。

1 她叫什么名字？

_____

2 她是哪国人？住在哪里？

_____

3 她在哪里工作？那里怎么样？

_____

Character reading

2 Match the radicals with the meanings.

1 衤   **a** shell

2 贝   **b** clothes

Now match the words with the meanings.

3 裙子   **c** expensive

4 衬衫   **d** shopping

5 贵   **e** skirt

6 购物   **f** shirt

Character writing

3 Make sentences using the words given.

1 购物   贵

_____

2 买   裙子

_____

Vocabulary extension

4 Write six sentences about your clothes, including their colours. Use the following words to help you.

wéijīn 围巾	chènshān 衬衫	duǎnkù 短裤
màozi 帽子	niúzǎikù 牛仔裤	liányīqún 连衣裙

1 _____

2 _____

3 _____

4 _____

5 _____

6 _____

CHARACTER WRITING

Objectives

1 Practise eight characters with the radicals 衤 and 贝

2 Learn to write eight common words for clothes, colours and places

1 Write the words containing the radicals 衤 and 贝.

qún *skirt*

裙	裙	裙	裙	裙	裙
裙	裙	裙	裙	裙	裙
裙					

kù *trousers*

裤	裤	裤	裤	裤	裤
裤	裤	裤	裤	裤	裤
裤					

chènshān *shirt*

衬	衬	衬	衬	衬	衬
衬	衬				
衬					

衫	衫	衫	衫	衫	衫
衫	衫				
衫					

shòuhuòyuán *shop assistant*

售	售	售	售	售	售
售	售	售	售	售	
售					

贷	贷	贷	贷	贷	贷
贷	贷				
贷					

员	员	员	员	员	员
员					
员					

guì *expensive*

贵	贵	贵	贵	贵	贵
贵	贵	贵			
贵					

gòu *buy*

购	购	购	购	购	购
购	购				
购					

2 Write the words following the correct stroke order.

yīfu *clothes*

衣 衣 衣 衣 衣 衣

衣

服 服 服 服 服 服
服 服

服

xié *shoes*

鞋 鞋 鞋 鞋 鞋 鞋
鞋 鞋 鞋 鞋 鞋 鞋
鞋 鞋 鞋

鞋

hóng *red*

红 红 红 红 红 红

红

hēi *black*

黑 黑 黑 黑 黑 黑
黑 黑 黑 黑 黑 黑

黑

lán *blue*

蓝 蓝 蓝 蓝 蓝 蓝
蓝 蓝 蓝 蓝 蓝 蓝
蓝

蓝

bái *white*

白 白 白 白 白

白

chāoshì *supermarket*

超 超 超 超 超 超
超 超 超 超 超 超

超

市 市 市 市 市

市

diàn *shop*

店 店 店 店 店 店
店 店

店

SELF-ASSESSMENT

Complete the checklist, using the criteria below.

1 = I need a lot of help to do this.   4 = I can do this very well.

2 = I can do this with a little help.   5 = I can do this almost perfectly.

3 = I can do this fairly well.

LANGUAGE SKILL	PROGRESS	YOUR SCORE
PRONUNCIATION	• I can identify and say the tones of 一 in different phrases.	
VOCABULARY	• I can name six colours. • I can name six items of clothing. • I can express prices correctly. • I know the words for four places where people can buy things.	
GRAMMAR	• I can use the measure words 个, 条, 件 and 双 correctly. • I can use 二 when counting or expressing sequence. • I can use 两 to express quantity. • I can use the particle 了 to express past tense.	
LISTENING	• I can identify clothes, colours and prices. • I can understand conversations about buying things.	
READING	• I know the meanings of the radicals 衤 and 贝. • I can understand descriptions of a product's price and colour.	
SPEAKING	• I can describe the colour and price of different clothes. • I can express likes and dislikes about clothes. • I can negotiate prices.	
WRITING	• I can write eight characters with the radicals 衤 and 贝, and eight common words for clothes, colours and places. • I can write simple blog entries about things I have bought.	

UNIT 9 不远!
Bù yuǎn

It's not far!

LESSON | 1

Objectives

1 **Vocabulary:** places in the neighbourhood

2 **Vocabulary:** directions and locations

3 **Conversation and listening:** identify locations and directions of places

4 **Conversation and listening:** ask for and give directions

5 **Pronunciation:** retroflex "r"

Vocabulary

1 Match the words with the meanings.

1 饭馆 *fànguǎn*　　　**a** post office

2 洗手间 *xǐshǒujiān*　　**b** bookshop

3 银行 *yínháng*　　　**c** restaurant

4 邮局 *yóujú*　　　**d** bank

5 书店 *shūdiàn*　　　**e** park

6 公园 *gōngyuán*　　　**f** toilet

Now complete the sentence with the words above.

7 我家附近有 _____ *Wǒ jiā fùjìn yǒu*

_____。

2 Look at the map and complete the sentences with the words in the box.

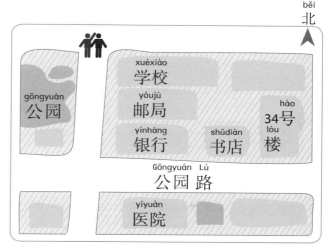

| dōngbian 东边 | běibian 北边 | xībian 西边 |
| fùjìn 附近 | nánbian 南边 | |

1 公园 在 邮局 的 _____。
Gōngyuán zài yóujú de

2 学校 在 邮局 的 _____。
Xuéxiào zài yóujú de

3 书店 在 银行 的 _____。
Shūdiàn zài yínháng de

4 医院 在 银行 的 _____。
Yīyuàn zài yínháng de

5 公园 路在 医院 的 _____。
Gōngyuán Lù zài yīyuàn de

6 34 号 楼在 书店 的 _____。
hào lóu zài shūdiàn de

Conversation and listening

3 Listen to the conversation and complete the sentences.

> **A:** 请问，中国银行在哪儿?
>
> **B:** 在医院前边。
>
> **A:** 离这儿远不远?
>
> **B:** 不远。
>
> **A:** 怎么走?
>
> **B:** 往东边走八分钟左右。
>
> **A:** 谢谢。

1 他要去 _____。

2 银行在医院 _____。

3 他要往 _____ 走 _____ 分钟。

4 Complete the conversation with the words in the box.

zài	yóujú	yǒu méiyǒu
在	邮局	有 没有
hòubian	nǎbiān	wǔ fēnzhōng
后边	哪边	五 分钟

> **A:** 请问，附近 (1) _____ 银行?
>
> **B:** 有，(2) _____ 上海路。
>
> **A:** 往 (3) _____ 走?
>
> **B:** 往西边走 (4) _____ ，在邮局
>
> (5) _____ 。
>
> **A:** 是公园前边的 (6) _____ 吗?
>
> **B:** 是的。

Now listen to the conversation and check the true statements.

☐ 7 附近没有银行。

☐ 8 银行在上海路。

☐ 9 上海路离这里很远。

☐ 10 上海路在西边。

☐ 11 邮局在公园的前边。

Pronunciation

5 Write pinyin for the words.

1 哪儿 _____

2 这儿 _____

3 那儿 _____

4 一点儿 _____

5 一块儿 _____

6 门口儿 _____

7 北边儿 _____

Now write sentences using the words given.

8 哪儿

_____

9 这儿

_____

10 那儿

_____

LESSON 2

Objectives

1 **Vocabulary:** types of housing

2 **Reading:** understand an advertisement for a flat

3 **Writing:** describe a flat you want to live in

4 **Grammar:** express existence using 有 (yǒu)

5 **Grammar:** ask questions using 有没有 (yǒu méiyǒu)

6 **Grammar:** express location with the verb 在 (zài)

本刊提醒在此刊登个人信息及使用本刊信

6 房屋信息 100 房屋出租

公寓出租

南京路28号5楼，80平方米，有两个房间。房子北边有公园，南边是购物中心。往西边走八分钟是地铁站，地铁站附近有超市，也有电影院。交通和买东西都很方便。

每月 ¥3200　电话：12928063715

联系人：王先生

Vocabulary

1 Number the words in the order you hear them.

□ **a** 公寓　　　　□ **e** 平方米

□ **b** 房子　　　　□ **f** 出租

□ **c** 房间　　　　□ **g** 地铁站

□ **d** 宿舍　　　　□ **h** 交通

Reading

2 Read the advertisement and complete the sentences.

1 房子在南京路 ＿＿＿＿ 号 ＿＿＿＿ 楼。

2 公寓不太大, 有 ＿＿＿＿＿＿＿。

3 公园在房子的 ＿＿＿＿＿＿＿。

4 地铁站在房子的 ＿＿＿＿＿＿＿。

5 买东西很方便，附近有 ＿＿＿＿＿＿

和 ＿＿＿＿＿＿。

Writing

3 Write a paragraph about the kind of flat you would like to live in.

＿＿＿＿＿＿＿＿＿＿＿＿＿＿＿＿＿＿＿

＿＿＿＿＿＿＿＿＿＿＿＿＿＿＿＿＿＿＿

＿＿＿＿＿＿＿＿＿＿＿＿＿＿＿＿＿＿＿

＿＿＿＿＿＿＿＿＿＿＿＿＿＿＿＿＿＿＿

＿＿＿＿＿＿＿＿＿＿＿＿＿＿＿＿＿＿＿

＿＿＿＿＿＿＿＿＿＿＿＿＿＿＿＿＿＿＿

Grammar

4 Put the words in the correct order to make sentences.

wǒ   méiyǒu   de   fángzi   chúfáng
1 我 / 没有 / 的 / 房子 / 厨房 /。

_____

yǒu   dōngbian   yīyuàn   de   xuéxiào
2 有 / 东边 / 医院 / 的 / 学校 /。

_____

chāoshì   qiánbian   gōngyuán   yǒu
3 超市 / 前边 / 公园 / 有 /。

_____

yínháng   méiyǒu   hòubian   yóujú
4 银行 / 没有 / 后边 / 邮局 /。

_____

méiyǒu   gòuwù zhōngxīn   fùjìn   diànyǐngyuàn
5 没有 / 购物 中心 / 附近 / 电影院 /。

_____

5 Write questions for the answers using 有没有.

Xuéxiào   fùjìn   yǒu   shūdiàn
1 学校 附近 有 书店。

_____

Gōngyuán nánbian yǒu fànguǎn
2 公园 南边 有 饭馆。

_____

Diànyǐngyuàn hòubian méiyǒu yínháng
3 电影院 后边 没有 银行。

_____

Yīyuàn de fùjìn méiyǒu chāoshì
4 医院 的附近 没有 超市。

_____

Dìtiě zhàn méiyǒu xǐshǒujiān
5 地铁 站 没有 洗手间。

_____

6 Write five sentences about the location of the places on the map using 在.

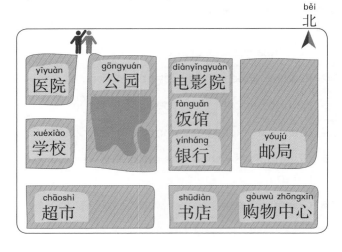

1 _____

2 _____

3 _____

4 _____

5 _____

Now rewrite the sentences using 有 or 在.

Diànyǐngyuàn zài gōngyuán dōngbian
6 电影院 在 公园 东边。
Gōngyuán
公园 _____ 。

Yīyuàn fùjìn méiyǒu yóujú
7 医院 附近 没有 邮局。
Yóujú
邮局 _____ 。

Xuéxiào zài gōngyuán de xībian
8 学校 在 公园 的 西边。
Gōngyuán
公园 _____ 。

Gòuwù zhōngxīn de běibian yǒu yóujú
9 购物 中心 的 北边 有 邮局。
yóujú
邮局 _____ 。

LESSON | 3

Objectives

1 **Reading:** understand descriptions of weekend activities

2 **Character reading:** recognize characters with the radicals 木 and 彳

3 **Character writing:** give directions

4 **Vocabulary extension:** places in the neighbourhood

Reading

38

1 Read Liu Li's email to her parents and check the true statements.

> ◀ 返回 ↺回复 ↺回复全部 🗗转发 ✖删除
>
> 爸爸妈妈：
>
> 　　你们好吗？
>
> 　　我在大学认识了很多朋友。周末我们一起去吃中餐。我最喜欢去学校附近的饭馆，那里的菜很好吃，价钱也不贵。
>
> 　　星期天，我跟朋友去超市买东西。超市离大学很近，走十分钟左右，很方便。
>
> 　　　　　　　　　　　刘丽

☐ 1 刘丽有很多朋友。

☐ 2 她喜欢跟朋友一起吃中餐。

☐ 3 学校附近饭馆的中餐很贵。

☐ 4 她跟朋友一起去超市。

☐ 5 超市离大学不远。

Character reading

2 Match the radicals with the meanings.

1 木　　　　**a** step

2 彳　　　　**b** tree

Now match the words with the meanings.

3 怎么样　　**c** lawyer

4 很　　　　**d** woods

5 林　　　　**e** how about

6 律师　　　**f** very

Character writing

3 Make sentences using the words given.

1 楼　　　　附近

_____

2 银行　　　往

_____

Vocabulary extension

4 Complete the table with the words in the box.

> shāngdiàn　　yàodiàn　　lǚguǎn
> 商店　　　　药店　　　旅馆
>
> jiànshēnfáng　jǐngchájú　kāfēidiàn
> 健身房　　　警察局　　咖啡店

Activities	Places
zhù 住 (live)	
hē kāfēi 喝 咖啡 (drink coffee)	
mǎi dōngxi 买 东西 (shopping)	
zuò yùndòng 做 运动 (exercise)	
qiúzhù 求助 (get help)	

CHARACTER WRITING

Objectives

1 Practise five characters with the radicals 木 and 彳

2 Learn to write nine common words for directions and types of student housing

1 Write the words containing the radicals 木 and 彳.

hěn *very*

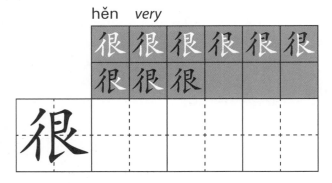

yínháng *bank*

wǎng *towards*

lóu *building, storey*

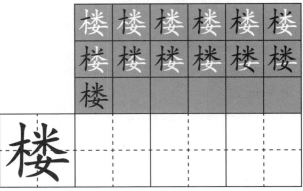

shǒujī *mobile phone*

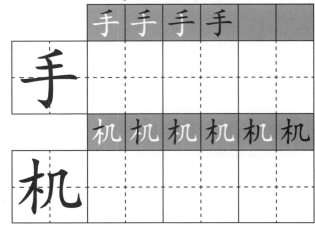

2 Write the words following the correct stroke order.

dōngbian *east*

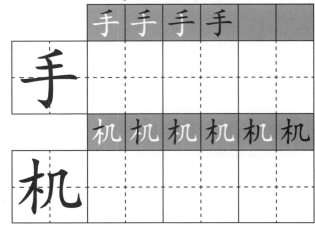

nán *south*

南 南 南 南 南 南
南 南 南

南

xī *west*

西 西 西 西 西 西

西

běi *north*

北 北 北 北 北

北

qián *front*

前 前 前 前 前 前
前 前 前

前

hòu *back*

后 后 后 后 后 后

后

fùjìn *vicinity, nearby*

附 附 附 附 附 附
附

附

近 近 近 近 近 近
近

近

fáng *house*

房 房 房 房 房 房
房 房

房

sùshè *dormitory*

宿 宿 宿 宿 宿 宿
宿 宿 宿 宿 宿

宿

舍 舍 舍 舍 舍 舍
舍 舍

舍

SELF-ASSESSMENT

Complete the checklist, using the criteria below.

1 = I need a lot of help to do this.   4 = I can do this very well.

2 = I can do this with a little help.   5 = I can do this almost perfectly.

3 = I can do this fairly well.

LANGUAGE SKILL	PROGRESS	YOUR SCORE
PRONUNCIATION	• I can identify and say words with retroflex "r".	
VOCABULARY	• I can give directions and describe locations. • I can name five places in a neighbourhood and three types of student housing.	
GRAMMAR	• I can express existence using 有. • I can ask questions using 有没有. • I can express location with the verb 在.	
LISTENING	• I can identify locations of and directions to places. • I can understand people describing locations and giving directions.	
READING	• I know the meanings of the radicals 木 and 彳. • I can recognize characters in advertisements for houses or flats. • I can understand descriptions of weekend activities.	
SPEAKING	• I can describe locations. • I can ask for and give directions.	
WRITING	• I can write five characters with the radicals 木 and 彳, and nine common words for directions and types of housing. • I can write a short description about my ideal flat.	

UNIT 10 坐火车吧。
Zuò huǒchē ba

Let's take the train.

LESSON | 1

Objectives

1 **Vocabulary:** means of transport
2 **Conversation and listening:** understand transport options
3 **Conversation and listening:** make an appointment
4 **Pronunciation:** difference between "q" and "ch"

Vocabulary

1 Find six means of transport in the table.

dì 地	tiě 铁	yī 一	gōng 公	hǎi 海
chū 出	shàng 上	zhōng 中	gòng 共	yuè 月
zū 租	dà 大	qí 骑	qì 汽	fāng 方
chē 车	zì 自	xíng 行	chē 车	xué 学
yuán 园	huǒ 火	xīn 心	zhàn 站	yóu 由
zǒu 走	chē 车	fēi 飞	jī 机	chǎng 场

1 _____   4 _____

2 _____   5 _____

3 _____   6 _____

Conversation and listening

2 Complete the conversation with the words in the box.

zuǒyòu 左右	háishi 还是	hěn yuǎn 很远
fāngbiàn 方便	zěnme 怎么	zěnmeyàng 怎么样

永民： (1) _____ 去三里屯? 坐地铁去 (2) _____?

安娜： 地铁站 (3) _____, 坐地铁不太 (4) _____。

永民： 坐出租车 (5) _____ 公共 汽车?

安娜： 坐出租车吧。十五分钟 (6) _____, 也不太贵。

永民： 好吧。

Now listen to the conversation and answer the questions.

7 永民要去哪里?

_____

8 他坐地铁去吗?

_____

9 附近有没有地铁站?

_____

10 他坐什么车去?

_____

11 这里离三里屯远吗? 坐出租车要多少
分钟?

_____

3 Listen to the conversation and check the true statements.

A: 这个星期你有时间吗? 我们一起
   吃饭。

B: 我明天有时间。

A: 好。明天几点?

B: 晚上七点, 可以吗?

A: 没问题。你喜欢中餐还是日本菜?

B: 吃中餐吧。我星期六吃了日本菜。

A: 我们去 "北京厨房", 好不好?

B: 好。明天七点在餐厅门口见。

☐ 1 他们明天一起吃饭。

☐ 2 他们七点到餐厅。

☐ 3 她不喜欢吃中餐, 她要吃日本菜。

Pronunciation

4 Check the correct pinyin for the words.

1 一起	☐ a yīchǐ	☐ b yīqǐ
2 裙子	☐ a qúnzi	☐ b chúnzi
3 请问	☐ a chénwèn	☐ b qǐngwèn
4 价钱	☐ a jiàqian	☐ b jiàchén
5 骑车	☐ a chí chē	☐ b qí chē
6 前边	☐ a qiánbian	☐ b chēbian
7 吃饭	☐ a qīfàn	☐ b chīfàn
8 出租车	☐ a chūzūchē	☐ b qūzūchē
9 唱歌	☐ a chànggē	☐ b qiànggē
10 超市	☐ a qiāoshì	☐ b chāoshì
11 厨房	☐ a qúfáng	☐ b chúfáng
12 船	☐ a chuán	☐ b quán

Now listen and check your answers. Then write sentences using the words given.

13 一起   骑车

_____

14 请问   前边

_____

15 出租车   超市

_____

LESSON | 2

Objectives

1 **Vocabulary:** holiday activities

2 **Reading:** understand people making travel plans

3 **Writing:** describe one's travel plans and make an invitation

4 **Grammar:** alternative questions with 还是 (háishì)

5 **Grammar:** questions ending with 好吗 (hǎoma)

6 **Grammar:** express superlatives with 最 (zuì)

7 **Grammar:** use the particle 吧 (ba)

Vocabulary

1 Match the words with the meanings.

zuò chuán
1 坐　船　　　　　a take photos

yóulǎn
2 游览　　　　　　b go sightseeing

páshān
3 爬山　　　　　　c climb a mountain

pāizhào
4 拍照　　　　　　d visit a scenic site

cānguān jǐngdiǎn
5 参观　景点　　　e take boat

Reading

2 Read Yeong-min's online conversation with Mark, and answer the questions.

1 永民和马克暑假要做什么?

_____

2 他们计划去哪里旅行?

_____

3 他们要坐船游览吗?

_____

4 他们怎么去桂林? 几月去?

_____

永民: 暑假一起去旅行好吗?

马克: 好。去哪里?

永民: 去桂林吧。那里很漂亮，有很多有名的景点。

马克: 桂林有什么景点?

永民: 我们问问王玉吧。她四月去了桂林，游览了漓江 (Li River)。

马克: 我们要坐船游览吗?

永民: 当然了! 坐船看景点很方便。

马克: 我们怎么去桂林? 坐火车还是飞机?

永民: 坐火车吧，便宜，我们也有时间。

马克: 好。几月几号去?

永民: 暑假第一个星期，七月二十号，怎么样?

马克: 我七月没有时间。八月第一个星期，可以吗?

永民: 好吧。

关闭（C）　发送（S）　▼

Writing

❸ Write an email to a friend, telling him/her your travel plans for the summer vacation. Invite him/her to go with you.

_____

_____

_____

Grammar

❹ Put the words in the correct order to make questions.

háishi nǐ yào qúnzi kùzi
1 还是 / 你 / 要 / 裙子 / 裤子 /?

_____

nǐ xǐhuan chī háishi Rìběncài Yìdàlìcài
2 你 / 喜欢 / 吃 / 还是 / 日本菜 / 意大利菜?

_____

háishi sān diǎn dǎ lánqiú sì diǎn
3 还是 / 三 点 / 打 篮球 / 四 点 /?

_____

nǐ háishi jīntiān yǒu shíjiān míngtiān
4 你 / 还是 / 今天 / 有 时间 / 明天 /?

_____

❺ Write the questions in Chinese using 好吗.

1 Shall we have Chinese food?

_____

2 Shall we take a taxi?

_____

3 Shall we go to see a movie on Friday evening?

_____

❻ Answer the questions using 最.

Nǐ zuì xǐhuan xīngqījǐ
1 你 最 喜欢 星期几?

_____

Shénme yánsè zuì piàoliang
2 什么 颜色 最 漂亮?

_____

Shénme zuì hǎochī
3 什么 最 好吃?

_____

Nǐ zuì xǐhuan shéi
4 你 最 喜欢 谁?

_____

❼ Translate the sentences into English.

Nǐ shìshi ba
1 你 试试 吧。

_____

Wǒmen qù tīng yīnyuèhuì ba
2 我们 去 听 音乐会 吧。

_____

Piányi yīdiǎnr ba
3 便宜 一点儿 吧。

_____

Jīntiān chī Rìběncài ba
4 今天 吃 日本菜 吧。

_____

Xīngqī' èr qù kàn diànyǐng ba
5 星期二 去 看 电影 吧。

_____

Zuò dìtiě ba   dìtiě fāngbiàn yīdiǎnr
6 坐 地铁 吧，地铁 方便 一点儿。

_____

LESSON | 3

Conversation and listening

1 Listen to the conversation and check the true statements.

> 史蒂夫： 美国银行前边有个意大利餐厅，你知道吗?
>
> 永民： 当然知道! 那个意大利餐厅很有名。
>
> 史蒂夫： 我们去那里吃饭，好吗?
>
> 永民： 太好了! 我最喜欢意大利菜。我们明天去吧。
>
> 史蒂夫： 我请两个朋友一起去,可以吗?
>
> 永民： 没问题。
>
> 史蒂夫： 我给朋友们打电话，请他们明天晚上七点到餐厅门口。
>
> 永民： 好。

☐ 1 史蒂夫和永民今天吃意大利菜。

☐ 2 这个餐厅不太有名。

☐ 3 餐厅离美国银行不远。

☐ 4 他们要跟朋友一起吃意大利菜。

☐ 5 他们明天晚上六点在餐厅门口见。

Character reading

2 Match the radicals with the meanings.

1 又   **a** eat

2 彳   **b** again

Now match the words with the meanings.

3 朋友   **c** hair

4 参观   **d** dinner

5 头发   **e** friend

6 晚饭   **f** visit

Character writing

3 Make sentences using the words given.

1 参观   景点

_____

2 饭馆   门口

_____

Vocabulary extension

4 Write sentences using the words given.

1 飞机场   火车站

_____

2 停车场   加油站

_____

CHARACTER WRITING

Objectives

1 Practise seven characters with the radicals 又 and 饣

2 Learn to write six common words for modes of transport and holiday activities

1 Write the words containing the radicals 又 and 饣.

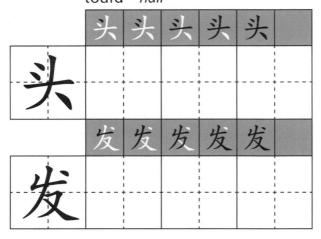

xǐhuan *like*

喜	喜	喜	喜	喜	喜
喜	喜	喜	喜	喜	喜
喜					
欢	欢	欢	欢	欢	欢
欢					

tóufa *hair*

头	头	头	头	头	
头					
发	发	发	发	发	
发					

duì *right, correct*

对	对	对	对	对	
对					

péngyou *friend*

朋	朋	朋	朋	朋	朋
朋	朋				
朋					
友	友	友	友		
友					

shuāng *pair*

双	双	双	双		
双					

fànguǎn *restaurant*

饭	饭	饭	饭	饭	饭
饭					
饭					
馆	馆	馆	馆	馆	馆
馆	馆	馆	馆	馆	
馆					

2 **Write the words following the correct stroke order.**

huǒchē   *train*

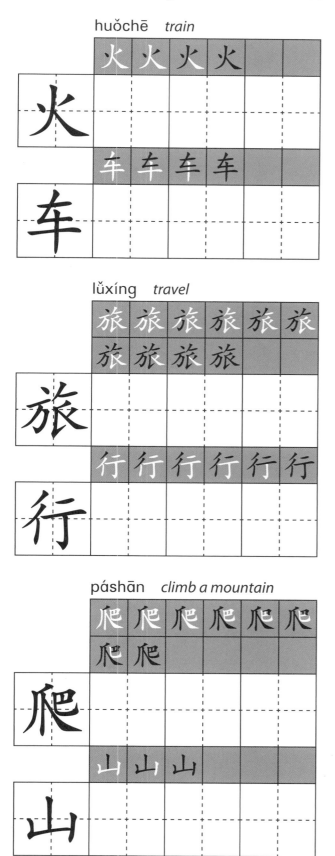

cānguān   *visit (a place)*

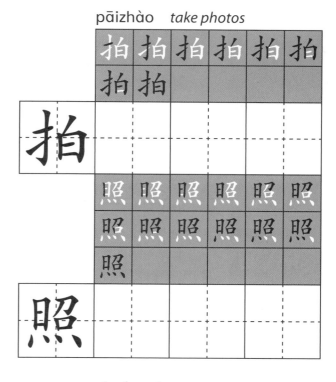

lǚxíng   *travel*

pāizhào   *take photos*

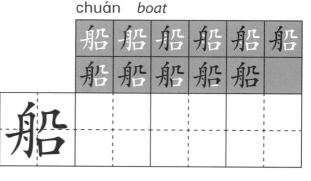

páshān   *climb a mountain*

chuán   *boat*

SELF-ASSESSMENT

Complete the checklist, using the criteria below.

1 = I need a lot of help to do this.

2 = I can do this with a little help.

3 = I can do this fairly well.

4 = I can do this very well.

5 = I can do this almost perfectly.

LANGUAGE SKILL	PROGRESS	YOUR SCORE
PRONUNCIATION	• I can identify and say words with the initials "q" and "ch".	
VOCABULARY	• I can name five types of transport. • I know the words to make plans and appointments. • I know five words for holiday activities.	
GRAMMAR	• I can ask alternative questions with 还是. • I can make a suggestion or ask for an opinion using 好吗. • I can express superlatives with 最. • I can use the particle 吧 to express commands or suggestions.	
LISTENING	• I can understand descriptions of different types of transport. • I can understand people talking about appointments and simple plans.	
READING	• I know the meanings of the radicals 又 and 饣. • I can recognize characters to understand simple travel plans and invitations.	
SPEAKING	• I can talk about different types of transport. • I can discuss which type of transport to take. • I can describe and make simple plans.	
WRITING	• I can write seven characters with the radicals 又 and 饣, and six common words for modes of transport and holiday activities. • I can write simple travel plans and invitations.	

UNIT 11

Wǒ huì tiàowǔ

我 会 跳舞。

I can dance.

LESSON | 1

Objectives

1 **Vocabulary:** types of sport, likes and dislikes

2 **Conversation and listening:** talk about sports and make appointments

3 **Conversation and listening:** talk about a football match and favourite player

4 **Pronunciation:** difference between "zh" and "ch"

Vocabulary

1 Write the sports in Chinese.

1 tennis   _____

2 table tennis   _____

3 football   _____

4 swimming   _____

5 basketball   _____

6 dancing   _____

Now complete the sentences with the words above.

Wǒ xǐhuan   bù xǐhuan

7 我 喜欢 _____, 不 喜欢 _____。

Wǒ de péngyou xǐhuan   bù xǐhuan

8 我 的 朋友 喜欢 _____, 不 喜欢

_____。

Conversation and listening

2 Complete the conversation with the words in the box.

zěnmeyàng 怎么样	wǎngqiú bǐsài 网球 比赛	ménkǒu 门口
huì bù huì 会不会	yǒu shíjiān 有 时间	xǐhuan 喜欢

永民： 星期天下午去看 (1) _____ 好吗?

安娜： 好! 我 (2) _____ 看网球比赛。

永民： 你 (3) _____ 打网球?

安娜： 当然会, 我打网球很不错。

永民： (4) _____ 我们一起去打网球吧。

安娜： 好。下个星期二下午你有时间吗?
我们去体育场打网球 (5) _____?

永民： 我有时间。我们三点在体育场
(6) _____ 见, 好吗?

安娜： 没问题。

44 Now listen to the conversation and check the true statements.

☐ 7 永民和安娜喜欢看网球比赛。

☐ 8 他们星期日去看比赛。

☐ 9 他们不会打网球。

☐ 10 他们星期二下午去体育场。

45 **3** Listen to the conversation and check the true statements.

永民：马克，星期二的足球比赛，
哪个球队赢了？

马克：当然是英格兰队赢了！

永民：我真希望是法国队赢！

马克：法国队不错，但是我喜欢英
格兰队。

永民：你最喜欢哪个运动员？

马克：我最喜欢英格兰队的David。

☐ 1 马克昨天看了足球比赛。

☐ 2 昨天是英格兰队赢。

☐ 3 马克和永民都希望英格兰队赢。

☐ 4 马克不喜欢英格兰队的运动员。

Pronunciation

46 **4** Check the correct initial for the characters.

		zh	ch
1	吃	a ☐	b ☐
2	出	a ☐	b ☐
3	唱	a ☐	b ☐
4	住	a ☐	b ☐
5	这	a ☐	b ☐
6	真	a ☐	b ☐
7	船	a ☐	b ☐
8	中	a ☐	b ☐

Now listen and check your answers. Then write pinyin for the words.

9 吃中餐 _____

10 超市 _____

11 冲浪 _____

12 城市 _____

13 知道 _____

14 分钟 _____

15 服装市场 _____

16 拍照 _____

LESSON | 2

Objectives

1 **Vocabulary:** recreational activities, types of sports

2 **Reading:** understand a blog entry about sports activities

3 **Communication:** conduct a class survey about sports

4 **Grammar:** use the modal verb 可以 (kěyǐ)

5 **Grammar:** use the modal verb 会 (huì)

6 **Grammar:** pivotal sentences

7 **Grammar:** talk about past actions with 过 (guò)

Vocabulary

1 Number the sports in the order you hear them.

□ a	qiánshuǐ 潜水	□ e	bèngjí 蹦极
□ b	lánqiú 篮球	□ f	huáxuě 滑雪
□ c	chōnglàng 冲浪	□ g	wǎngqiú 网球
□ d	pīngpāngqiú 乒乓球	□ h	pǎobù 跑步

Reading

2 Complete the questionnaire with information from Yeong-min's blog.

wǒ de xiūxián yùndòng
我 的 休闲 运动

主页 | 博客 | 相册 | 档案 | 互动 | Next

我叫永民。今年十八岁。我是韩国人，现在住在北京大学附近的公寓。我喜欢跑步，每天早上跑三十分钟。每个星期三上午我跟朋友踢足球。每个星期五下午我跟史蒂夫在大学的体育场打篮球。我不喜欢在健身房做运动。我不会游泳，希望下个月开始学游泳。

分享 | 评论 (16) | 阅读 (476) | 固定链接 | 发表于 15:36

学生运动和休闲问卷

姓名：_____
年龄：_____
性别：_____
国籍：_____

你喜欢什么运动？
踢足球 □   冲浪 □
游泳 □   滑雪 □
打篮球 □   潜水 □
打乒乓球 □   蹦极 □
其他 □

你每星期做多少个小时运动？
□ 0   □ 1-2   □ 3-4   □ 5-10

你什么时候做运动？ _____
你和谁一起做运动？ _____
你在哪里做运动？
□ 家里   □ 健身房   □ 体育场

Communication

3 Use the questionnaire in Activity 2 to conduct a survey on your classmates' recreational activities.

Now complete the sentences using your survey results.

Tóngxuémen zuì xǐhuan de yùndòng shì
1 同学们 最 喜欢 的 运动 是 _____
_____。

Tóngxuémen zuì bù xǐhuan de yùndòng shì
2 同学们 最 不 喜欢 的 运动 是 ____
_____。

Tóngxuémen měi xīngqī zuì duō zuò   gè
3 同学们 每 星期 最 多 做 _____ 个
xiǎoshí yùndòng
小时 运动。

Grammar

4 Write questions for the answers .

Nǐ shǔjià kěyǐ qù Guìlín lǚxíng
1 你 暑假 可以 去 桂林 旅行。

_____

Nǐ kěyǐ gěi lǎoshī xiě diànzǐ yóujiàn
2 你 可以 给 老师 写 电子 邮件。

_____

Nǐ kěyǐ lái wǒ de shēngrì pàiduì
3 你 可以 来 我 的 生日 派对。

_____

5 Write the sentences in Chinese.

1 Can you swim?

_____

2 We can't play basketball.

_____

3 They can dance.

_____

6 Put the words in the correct order to make sentences.

yīnyuèhuì Shǐdìfū Ānnà tīng qǐng
1 音乐会 / 史蒂夫 / 安娜 / 听 / 请 / 。

_____

wǒ Yīnggélán duì yíng xīwàng
2 我 / 英格兰 队 / 赢 / 希望 / 。

_____

chī Wáng lǎoshī qǐng Rìběncài wǒmen
3 吃 / 王 老师 / 请 / 日本菜 / 我 们 / 。

_____

qǐng tiàowǔ Wáng Yù Yǒngmín
4 请 / 跳舞 / 王 玉 / 永民 / 。

_____

xīwàng péngyǒu tā dǎ diànhuà gěi tā
5 希望 / 朋友 / 他 / 打 电话 / 给 他 / 。

_____

7 Put 过 in the correct places in the sentences.

Wǒ mèimei qù Jiānádà
1 我 妹妹 去 加拿大。

_____

Mǎkè méi xué dǎ wǎngqiú
2 马克 没 学 打 网球。

_____

Mǎ yīshēng de dìdi zuò jìzhě
3 马 医生 的 弟弟 做 记者。

_____

Tāmen qù Běijīng Sānlǐtún
4 他们 去 北京 三里屯。

_____

Wǒmen cānguān hěn duō jǐngdiǎn
5 我们 参观 很 多 景点。

_____

LESSON | 3

Objectives

1 **Conversation:** talk about a recreational class

2 **Character reading:** recognize characters with the radicals 王 and 钅

3 **Character writing:** describe recreational activities

4 **Vocabulary extension:** different types of sport

Conversation

1 Match the questions with the answers.

1 什么时间? _____

2 学跳舞多少钱? _____

3 学校在哪里? _____

4 我们一起学跳舞好吗? _____

a 在北京大学的东边, 购物中心的三楼。

b 每星期四晚上八点。

c 好, 我喜欢跳舞。

d 一小时五十块。

Now put the sentences in the correct order to make a conversation.

The correct order is _____.

Character reading

2 Match the radicals with the meanings.

1 王   a metal

2 钅   b jade

Now match the words with the meanings.

3 希望   c price

4 地铁   d sports team

5 球队   e subway

6 价钱   f hope

Character writing

3 Make sentences using the words given.

1 周末   足球

_____

2 喜欢   游泳

_____

Vocabulary extension

4 Answer the questions with the words in the boxs.

lánqiú 篮球	qūgùnqiú 曲棍球	wǎngqiú 网球	páiqiú 排球
bàngqiú 棒球	huáxuě 滑雪	bèngjí 蹦极	zúqiú 足球
chōnglàng 冲浪	gǎnlǎnqiú 橄榄球	qiánshuǐ 潜水	yóuyǒng 游泳
pǎobù 跑步	pīngpāngqiú 乒乓球		

Nǐ huì shénme yùndòng
1 你 会 什么 运动?

_____

Nǐ xǐhuan shénme yùndòng
2 你 喜欢 什么 运动?

_____

Nǐ xiǎng kàn shénme bǐsài
3 你 想 看 什么 比赛?

_____

CHARACTER WRITING

Objectives

1 Practise six characters with the radicals 王 and 钅

2 Learn to write seven common words for abilities and types of sport

1 Write the words containing the radicals 王 and 钅.

wán   *play*

玩 玩 玩 玩 玩 玩
玩 玩

玩

xiànzài   *now*

现 现 现 现 现 现
现 现

现

在 在 在 在 在 在

在

bān   *measure word, class*

班 班 班 班 班 班
班 班 班 班

班

zúqiú   *football*

足 足 足 足 足 足
足

足

球 球 球 球 球 球
球 球 球 球 球

球

qián   *money*

钱 钱 钱 钱 钱 钱
钱 钱 钱 钱

钱

dìtiě   *underground railway, subway*

地 地 地 地 地 地

地

铁 铁 铁 铁 铁 铁
铁 铁 铁 铁

铁

2 **Write the words following the correct stroke order.**

kěyǐ *can*

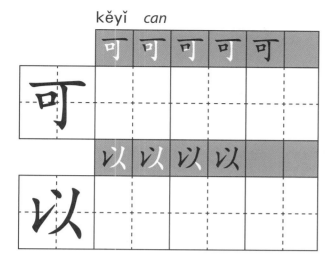

| 可 | 可 | 可 | 可 | 可 | |

可

| 以 | 以 | 以 | 以 | | |

以

huì *can, be able to*

| 会 | 会 | 会 | 会 | 会 | 会 |

会

yóuyǒng *swim*

| 游 | 游 | 游 | 游 | 游 | 游 |
| 游 | 游 | 游 | 游 | 游 | 游 |

游

| 泳 | 泳 | 泳 | 泳 | 泳 | 泳 |
| 泳 | 泳 | | | | |

泳

wǎngqiú *tennis*

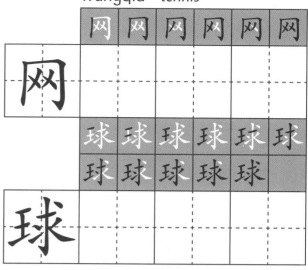

| 网 | 网 | 网 | 网 | 网 | 网 |

网

| 球 | 球 | 球 | 球 | 球 | 球 |
| 球 | 球 | 球 | 球 | 球 | |

球

tī *play (with feet), kick*

踢	踢	踢	踢	踢	踢
踢	踢	踢	踢	踢	踢
踢	踢	踢			

踢

pīngpāng *table tennis*

| 乒 | 乒 | 乒 | 乒 | 乒 | 乒 |

乒

| 兵 | 兵 | 兵 | 兵 | 兵 | 兵 |

兵

SELF-ASSESSMENT

Complete the checklist, using the criteria below.

1 = I need a lot of help to do this.   4 = I can do this very well.

2 = I can do this with a little help.   5 = I can do this almost perfectly.

3 = I can do this fairly well.

LANGUAGE SKILL	PROGRESS	YOUR SCORE
PRONUNCIATION	• I can identify and say words with the initials "zh" and "ch".	
VOCABULARY	• I can name five types of sport. • I can name five different recreational activities.	
GRAMMAR	• I can use the modal verb 可以 to talk about ability, possibility and permission. • I can use the modal verb 会 to talk about the ability to do something. • I can use pivotal sentences to express an invitation or wish. • I can use the particle 过 to talk about past actions.	
LISTENING	• I can identify different sports and recreational activities in a conversation. • I can understand people's descriptions of the sports they like and dislike.	
READING	• I know the meanings of the radicals 王 and 纟. • I can understand simple questionnaires and blog entries about sports and recreational activities.	
SPEAKING	• I can talk about sports activities I like and dislike.	
WRITING	• I can write six characters with the radicals 王 and 纟, and seven common words for abilities and sports. • I can describe my favourite sports and recreational activities. • I can complete a simple questionnaire about sports and recreational activities.	

UNIT 12

Wǒmen qù kàn jīngjù

我们 去 看 京剧。

We're going to the Beijing opera.

LESSON | 1

Objectives

1 **Vocabulary:** holiday activities

2 **Conversation and listening:** talk about holiday plans

3 **Pronunciation:** sentence intonation

4 **Grammar:** plans, past actions, alternatives, suggestions, times and abilities

Vocabulary

1 Match the words with the meanings.

huíjiā
1 回家   **a** go shopping

kàn jīngjù
2 看 京剧   **b** go back home

qù lǚxíng
3 去 旅行   **c** go to a concert

tīng yīnyuèhuì
4 听 音乐会   **d** go travelling

gòuwù
5 购物   **e** climb a mountain

páshān
6 爬山   **f** watch Beijing opera

Now write two sentences with some of the words above.

7 _____

8 _____

Conversation and listening

2 Put the sentences in the correct order to make a conversation.

a 我六月去过新加坡。那里很不错, 有很好的购物中心, 东西的价钱也不贵。

b 你去新加坡做什么?

c 安娜, 这个假期你打算去什么地方旅行?

d 太好了! 我喜欢购物。

e 十二月有我喜欢的音乐会, 我想去听音乐会。

f 我打算去新加坡。

The correct order is _____.

Now listen to the conversation and answer the questions.

1 安娜假期打算去哪里?

_____

2 什么时候有安娜喜欢的音乐会?

_____

3 安娜想在那里做什么?

_____

4 那里的购物中心怎么样?

_____

5 永民去过新加坡吗?

_____

Pronunciation

3 Mark the intonation for the sentences using ↑ (rising tone) and ↓ (falling tone).

Gēge jīntiān huíjiā ma
1 哥哥 今天 回家 吗? _____

Bié qù Jiānádà le   tài yuǎn le
2 别去加拿大了,太 远 了! _____

Nǐ jiàqī dǎsuan qù Rìběn ma
3 你 假期 打算 去 日本 吗? _____

Wǒ yào gěi Ānnà xiě diànzǐ yóujiàn
4 我 要 给 安娜 写 电子 邮件。 _____

Wǒ zuò fēijī qù   nǐ ne
5 我 坐 飞机 去, 你 呢? _____

Nǐ de gōngyù lí dàxué yuǎn ma
6 你 的 公寓 离 大学 远 吗? _____

Wǒ jiějie xǐhuan chī Zhōngcān
7 我 姐姐 喜欢 吃 中餐。 _____

Wǒ zhōumò qù kàn yéye nǎinai
8 我 周末 去 看 爷爷 奶奶。 _____

Now listen and check your answers.

Grammar

4 Translate the sentences into English.

Nǐ kàn guo jīngjù ma
1 你 看 过 京剧 吗?

_____

Nǐ dǎsuan zài Lúndūn zuò shénme
2 你 打算 在 伦敦 做 什么?

_____

Nǐ xiǎng chī Zhōngcān háishi Rìběncài
3 你 想 吃 中餐 还是 日本菜?

_____

Nǐ shénme shíhou qù shūdiàn
4 你 什么 时候 去 书店?

_____

Zhōumò yīqǐ qù kàn diànyǐng zěnmeyàng
5 周末 一起 去 看 电影, 怎么样?

_____

Zhè ge chāoshì de dōngxi hěn guì   bié qù le
6 这 个 超市 的 东西 很 贵, 别去了。

_____

Wǒmen yīqǐ qù lǚxíng   hǎo ma
7 我们 一起 去 旅行, 好 吗?

_____

Bàba jǐ diǎn huíjiā
8 爸爸 几 点 回家?

_____

Nǐ huì bù huì dǎ wǎngqiú
9 你 会 不 会 打 网球?

_____

Wǒ Xīngqīliù mǎi le yī tiáo hóng qúnzi
10 我 星期六 买 了 一 条 红 裙子。

_____

LESSON | 2

Objectives

1 **Vocabulary:** cities in China and places of interest

2 **Grammar:** express alternatives using 或者 (huòzhě)

3 **Grammar:** express alternatives using 或者 (huòzhě) and 还是 (háishi)

4 **Reading:** understand simple online chat messages about holiday plans

5 **Writing:** suggest a place to visit

6 **Grammar:** express regular events with 每……都…… (měi … dōu …)

Vocabulary

1 Write eight words about cities and places of interest using the characters in the table.

lì	guǎng	xiāng	shǐ	bīng
历	广	香	史	兵
xī	mǎ	shàng	shì	cháng
西	马	上	市	长
hǎi	běi	ān	yǒng	nián
海	北	安	俑	年
gǎng	zhōu	chéng	qiān	jīng
港	州	城	千	京

1 _____   5 _____

2 _____   6 _____

3 _____   7 _____

4 _____   8 _____

Grammar

2 Put the words in the correct order to make sentences.

nǐmen zuò qù dìtiě huòzhě gōnggòng
1 你们 / 坐 / 去 / 地铁 / 或者 / 公共
qìchē
汽车 / 。

_____

Xīngqīyī huòzhě yéye kàn Xīngqīsān qù
2 星期一 / 或者 / 爷爷 / 看 / 星期三 / 去
yīshēng
/ 医生 / 。

_____

yígè huòzhě tā yǒu gēge jiějie
3 一个 / 或者 / 他 / 有 / 哥哥 / 姐姐 / 。

_____

Měiguórén huòzhě shì Jiānádàrén tāmen
4 美国人 / 或者 / 是 / 加拿大人 / 他们 / 。

_____

3 Choose the correct words to complete the sentences.

Nǐ xǐhuan hēisè háishi huòzhě lánsè
1 你 喜欢 黑色 (还是 / 或者) 蓝色？

Jiàqī wǒ qù Měiguó háishi huòzhě Yīngguó
2 假期 我 去 美国 (还是 / 或者) 英国
lǚxíng
旅行。

Shí diǎn háishi huòzhě shí diǎn bàn dōu
3 十 点 (还是 / 或者) 十 点 半 都
kěyǐ
可以。

Tā shì lǎoshī háishi huòzhě xuésheng
4 她 是 老师 (还是 / 或者) 学生？

Reading

4 Read Yeong-min's online conversation with Steve and Mark.

👤 永民

暑假我打算跟朋友去英国或者澳大利亚旅行。两个地方我都没有去过。你们觉得哪个地方好玩？

👤 史蒂夫

英国不错！伦敦有很多有名的景点，购物的地方也很多。

👤 永民

我不太喜欢买东西。去景点的交通方便吗？

👤 史蒂夫

伦敦的地铁很方便，你也可以坐公共汽车或者出租车。

👤 马克

去澳大利亚吧。我有很多朋友在澳大利亚。你可以跟他们学潜水，很好玩。

👤 永民

好主意，我喜欢潜水！我应该去悉尼还是墨尔本呢？

👤 马克

去悉尼吧。那里的海很漂亮。

关闭（C） 发送（S） ▼

Now complete the sentences.

1 暑假永民打算跟 _____ 去旅行。

2 永民想去 _____ 或者 _____ 旅行。

3 史蒂夫说去 _____，那里有 _____ 和 _____。

4 在伦敦可以坐 _____，_____，或者 _____ 游览景点。

5 马克说去 _____，在那里可以 _____。

Writing

5 Write a message to Yeong-min, suggesting a place to go and what he can do there.

_____

_____

_____

_____

Grammar

6 Rewrite the sentences using 每……都…….

Wǒ jīntiān xué Zhōngwén
1 我 今天 学 中文。

_____

Xīngqīwǔ diànyǐngyuàn yǒu Měiguó diànyǐng
2 星期五 电影院 有 美国 电影。

_____

Mǎkè gēn Wáng Yù zhōumò dǎ wǎngqiú
3 马克 跟 王 玉 周末 打 网球。

_____

Xiānggǎng de dìtiězhàn yǒu yínháng
4 香港 的 地铁站 有 银行。

_____

LESSON | 3

Objectives

1 **Conversation and listening:** talk about travel experiences

2 **Character reading:** recognize characters with the radicals ⺮ and 禾

3 **Character writing:** make plans for recreational activities

4 **Vocabulary extension:** holiday activities

Conversation and listening

52

1 Listen to the conversation and check the correct answers.

安娜： 你去过中国哪几个城市？

永民： 我去过北京、上海和桂林。

安娜： 哪个城市最好玩？

永民： 每个城市都有很多景点，购物也很方便。三个地方都好玩。

安娜： 哪个城市历史最长？

永民： 北京。

安娜： 你最喜欢哪个城市？

永民： 我最喜欢桂林。

1 永民没去过什么城市？

　　□ a 西安　　□ b 北京　　□ c 桂林

2 哪个城市最好玩？

　　□ a 北京　　□ b 上海

　　□ c 三个地方都好玩

3 他最喜欢哪个城市？

　　□ a 北京　　□ b 上海　　□ c 桂林

Character reading

2 Match the radicals with the meanings.

1 ⺮　　　　　a grain

2 禾　　　　　b bamboo

Now match the words with the meanings.

3 出租车　　　c engineer

4 电子邮箱　　d email inbox/address

5 打算　　　　e taxi

6 工程师　　　f plan

Character writing

3 Make sentences using the words given.

1 打算　　　意大利

　_____

2 和　　　　篮球

　_____

Vocabulary extension

4 Write four sentences using the words in the box.

dǎgōng	zuò zhìyuànzhě
打工	做　志愿者
shíxí	yěyíng
实习	野营

1 _____

2 _____

3 _____

4 _____

CHARACTER WRITING

Objectives

1 Practise five characters with the radicals 竹 and 禾

2 Learn to write six common words for places and holiday activities

1 Write the words containing the radicals 竹 and 禾.

dǎsuan   *plan*

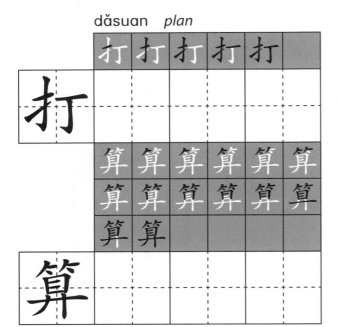

lánqiú   *basketball*

hé   *and*

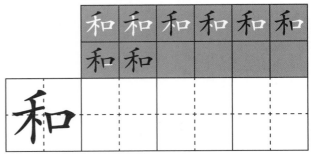

zū   *rent*

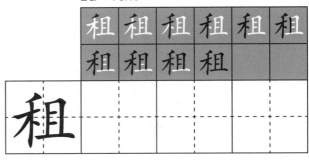

Xiānggǎng   *Hong Kong*

2 **Write the words following the correct stroke order.**

dìfang *place*

地	地	地	地	地	地

地

方	方	方	方		

方

chéngshì *city*

城	城	城	城	城	城
城	城	城			

城

市	市	市	市	市	

市

Xī'ān *Xi'an*

西	西	西	西	西	西

西

安	安	安	安	安	安

安

hǎowán *fun*

好	好	好	好	好	好

好

玩	玩	玩	玩	玩	玩
玩	玩				

玩

lìshǐ *history*

历	历	历	历		

历

史	史	史	史	史	

史

zhǔyì *idea*

主	主	主	主	主	

主

意	意	意	意	意	意
意	意	意	意	意	意
意					

意

SELF-ASSESSMENT

Complete the checklist, using the criteria below.

1 = I need a lot of help to do this.
2 = I can do this with a little help.
3 = I can do this fairly well.

4 = I can do this really well.
5 = I can do this almost perfectly.

LANGUAGE SKILL	PROGRESS	YOUR SCORE
PRONUNCIATION	• I can say sentences with the correct intonation.	
VOCABULARY	• I can say the names of five cities in China. • I can name five holiday activities. • I know common words and phrases to describe holiday plans and activities.	
GRAMMAR	• I can use 或者 and 还是 to express alternatives. • I can use 每……都…… to express regular events.	
LISTENING	• I can identify people's holiday preferences. • I can understand people talking about holiday plans.	
READING	• I know the meanings of the radicals ⺮ and 禾. • I can recognize the characters to understand chat messages about holiday plans.	
SPEAKING	• I can ask and answer questions about holiday plans. • I can express preferences for holiday plans.	
WRITING	• I can write five characters with the radicals ⺮ and 禾, and six common words for places and holiday activities. • I can suggest a place to visit and the things to do there.	

MY NOTES: